Acknowledgments

I0005642

The author wishes to thank the following people for helping make this book possible:

Technical Material:

- PACO/Grundfos
- Liquid Metronics, Inc.

Peer Review:

- Dave Davis, Sunrise Water Authority
- Alan Schacht, Sunrise Water Authority

Graphics:

- Tim Douglas

Word Processing and Organization:

- Nancy Jelinek

About the Author

Mr. Phil Beverly has a B.S. degree in Engineering from the Virginia Polytechnic Institute. He has professional licenses in civil, mechanical, and environmental engineering. He is also a certified Water Rights Examiner and a Level 3 Water Treatment Plant Operator with the filter endorsement in the State of Oregon. He has served on the AWWA B604 Standards Counsel Subcommittee for Granular Activated Carbon and Filter Media and is currently serving on the regional AWWA Seminars Committee. He was on the Environmental Registry *Who's Who*, 1992.

Mr. Beverly has more than 35 years experience in troubleshooting pumps and filters in both water and wastewater applications. He has helped rehabilitate approximately 200 filter plants and has been retained as a special consultant to resolve problems in numerous filtration and pumping facilities for water and wastewater treatment systems across the United States.

Mr. Beverly's background includes working for several water/ wastewater equipment suppliers and several consulting engineering companies. As part of that experience, he operated a research lab for an equipment supplier, which resulted in his obtaining three patents on filter underdrain improvements.

Mr. Beverly's services are provided by Process Consulting and Troubleshooting, L.L.C., in Elgin, Oregon. To contact the author, call 541-786-0907 or 541-437-2402.

The American Water Works Association published Mr. Beverly's book, *Filter Troubleshooting and Design Handbook*, in 2005. The handbook describes basic gravity filter design, including layering the support gravel, types of media, driving head, underdrain hydraulics, controls, and backwash optimization. Both handbooks are available at www.awwa.org/bookstore.

Introduction

A water system consists of many components, including a power supply, electrical wiring, switchgear, motor starters, the pumps themselves, a piping network or distribution system to deliver the water, storage reservoirs, and system controls. For these reasons, pumps should be evaluated according to the needs of the system. All the components must be sized and selected properly for the system to operate correctly.

The factors used to size a pump include flow (Q-gpm), pressure (H – head in feet), and motor horsepower (HP). These factors are of most interest to operation and maintenance (O&M) personnel. Once a pump has been designed and installed, the flow and pressure are the factors most easily verified by an operator. Other factors, such as pump type, impeller size, bearing selection, etc., are normally the province of the designer or manufacturer.

Pumps are usually the most expensive part of a water system to operate. Even so, they are easy to neglect when they are operating properly or seem to be. Pumps can also be very expensive to repair or replace after a failure. Such repairs can be time consuming and take staff away from other important duties. The author is aware of one facility where the water storage in the system was nearly depleted while an essential pump was being replaced. No fire flow capacity was available during that time as well.

It is the intent of this handbook to provide quick and easy methods to determine whether a pump is operating properly. For example, by using a pump's *family of curves* (the complete set of curves for a particular pump), it is possible to evaluate a pump's performance using a pressure gauge and flowmeter, and by touch. Information in this handbook describes pump operation and how the factors (flow, discharge pressing, and horsepower) can be easily used to evaluate performance. O&M personnel do not necessarily need to know how to design a pump, but it would be helpful to be able to read the family of curves and understand their meaning.

The handbook is organized into six chapters, as follows:

Chapter 1 – Pump Horsepower

Procedures for calculating horsepower required for a pump are

1

described. By using the family of curves, a determination can be made whether a pump is operating in the proper range.

Chapter 2 – Pump Types

Reading and understanding pump curves is discussed, and several common pump types are described, along with operational guidelines and methods of evaluating pump performance by touch and by using a pressure gauge and flowmeter.

Chapter 3 – Variable Flow

The effects of varying the flow in a pump by throttling or changing speed are discussed, along with the benefits of each.

Chapter 4 – Pump Troubleshooting

Methods of identifying typical pump problems are discussed, together with common solutions.

Chapter 5 – Chemical Pumps

Feed systems for common types of chemicals are discussed, along with sizing criteria and O&M recommendations. Typical problems and solutions are also presented.

Chapter 6 – Operation and Maintenance Manual

Reference information is recommended for on-site records.

CHAPTER 1

Pump Horsepower

Introduction

Once a pump is operating correctly, it should continue to do so if it is maintained properly and the system conditions remain the same. However, the available horsepower may limit the operating range of a pump. For example, changes in the demand of the system may require an increase in horsepower, or even a new pump.

Calculations should be kept on site to allow a quick review of the sizing of a pump and motor. If there are changes, or if a pump is not operating properly, the sizing criteria can quickly be reviewed for compliance. Although O&M personnel do not normally have to make those calculations, they have been included in operator certification tests. The most important procedure is the ability to use horsepower information to read a pump curve. This chapter and Chapter 2 demonstrate how this is performed. Information should be available to O&M staff for this purpose.

Performance

The performance factors of a pump need to be calculated during design and used for evaluation. The factors include the design flow (Q), usually expressed in gallons per minute, and pressure (or head) in pounds per square inch or feet of water. Q is determined by the process requirement, and is different for each installation. The pressure or head required for the pump discharge includes the sum of the static head and friction loss caused by piping, valves, fittings, flowmeters, etc. A general discussion of discharge pressure (pressure boost) is included to determine the horsepower for a pump.

It is important to understand that the discharge pressure of a pump alone is usually *not* an indication of the power/pressure added by the pump. The pressure boost (pressured added) has to take into account the suction side pressure. For example, if the discharge pressure of a pump is 100 psi, and the suction side pressure is 20 psi (flooded suction), the pressure boost by the pump is 80 psi (100 − 20).

With a suction lift of 5 psi and a discharge pressure of 100 psi, the pressure boost would be 105 psi (100 + 5).

The design (normal) discharge pressure, the normal suction side pressure, and the normal pressure boost should be identified for O&M personnel in the recommended on-site O&M manual. The following discussion is intended to help O&M personnel understand these terms and how they are calculated.

Static Head

The pumping height, or static head, is illustrated in Figure 1-1. The pumping height is the vertical distance from the original water surface to the finished water surface, whether the pump has a suction lift or a positive suction head (flooded suction). For a conservative approach, it is important that the maximum level of the receiving reservoir be used for design, along with the lowest level of the water source. Figure 1-2 illustrates the variation that can occur in the original water source. For example, in a deep well pump, it is common for a significant drawdown to occur when the pump is started up, and the final pumping level anticipated should be used for calculation purposes.

Friction Loss

Once a system has been designed, the friction loss can be calculated from the length of pipe and the number of fittings, valves, flowmeters and other devices in the line. It should be noted that pump control valves or other pieces of equipment can generate a significant head loss at the design flow. The individual manufacturer's literature is used to obtain that information. The allowance for friction loss should be included in the designer's calculations and included in the recommended on-site O&M manual. The total pump pressure (H) is the sum of the maximum static head (or vertical lift from water level to water level), the total friction loss, and the velocity head.

Pump Pressure – (Pump Boost H-ft) =
(Vertical lift + friction loss + dynamic pressure)
(An adaption of Bernoulli's Equation)

The **static discharge head** (H) that a pump must overcome is the vertical elevation gain (lift) from the pump to the discharge water level. The static head (lift) can be measured by a pressure gauge adjacent to the pump when it is *not* in operation.

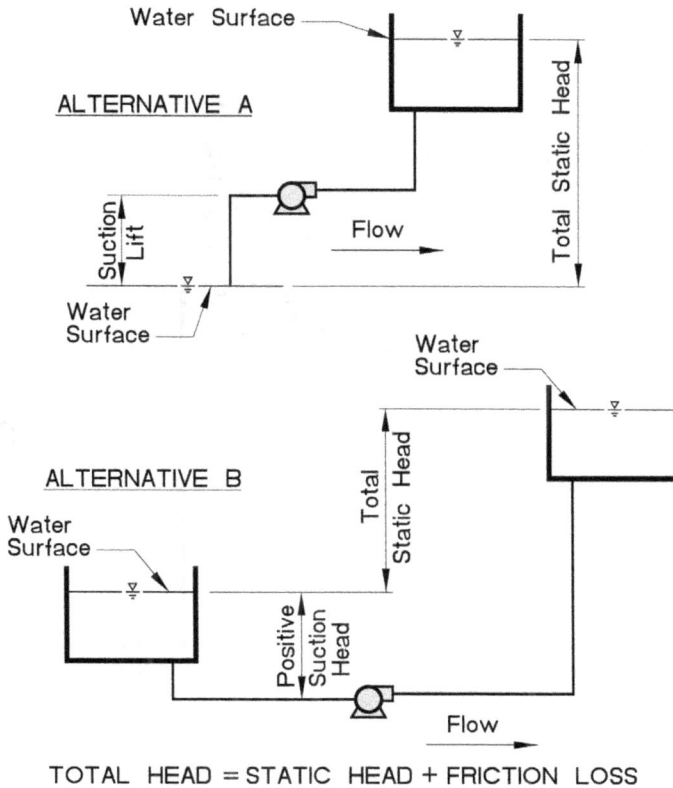

Figure 1-1   Typical centrifugal pump systems

The vertical lift is the difference from the intake water level to the discharge water level, as shown on Figure 1-1. With a flooded suction, the vertical lift (water level to water level) can be measured as the difference in the static pressure measured by pressure gauges on both sides of a pump when it is *not* in operation (assuming there is a check valve on the pump discharge). In a suction lift condition, the lift from the water source to the pump must be added to the static head to calculate the vertical lift.

Friction loss is the force, or pressure loss, required to push water to the discharge point or water level. The total amount of friction is the sum of the loss through the piping, valves, elbows, tees, and other fittings between the pump and the discharge point.

Dynamic pressure is the force required to move water through

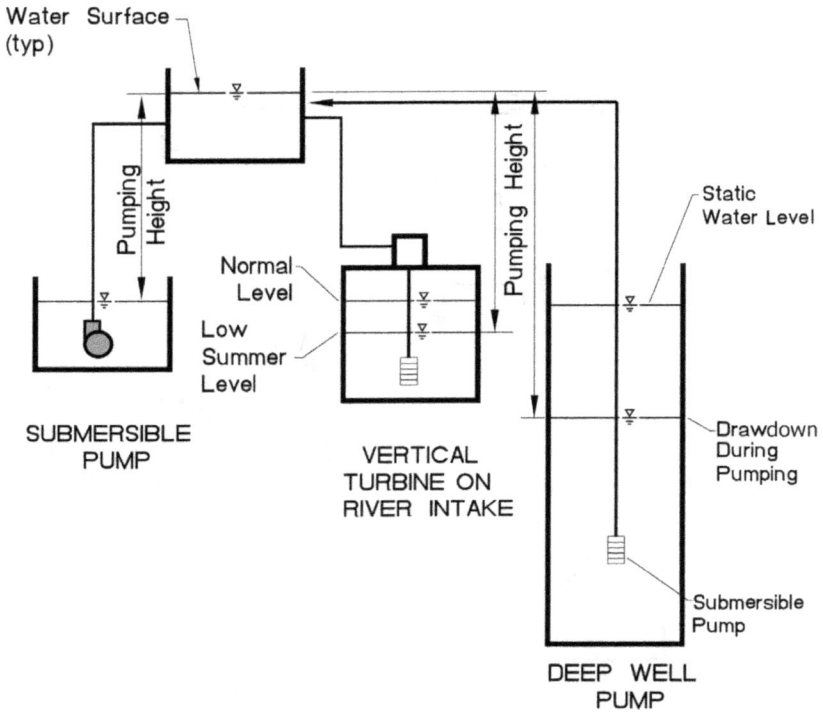

Figure 1-2   Pumping height miscellaneous pumps

a pipe at a specific velocity. The value for dynamic loss can be found in a hydraulic handbook for piping. If the pipe size is adequate and the velocity is low, the dynamic pressure is usually not a large value.

Total discharge pressure, the total pressure that a pump operates against, can be measured by a pressure gauge close to the pump *while it is operating.* The total discharge pressure, as measured, includes the static lift, friction loss, and dynamic pressure. It should be noted that this pressure only pertains to the flow (Q) at the time of the measurement.

Note: It is not intended for the operator to make these calculations. Each individual item should be compiled by the designer and included in the recommended pump manual to be available at the site.

The **pressure boost** is the power input by the pump. It is the total discharge pressure minus any positive suction pressure, or plus any negative suction pressure. As always, the pressure boost is from water level to water level. The pressure boost is the value that must be used when referring to the pump operational curve.

Pump and motor efficiencies are factors that also affect the pump horsepower and will be discussed further on in this handbook.

Horsepower Definitions and Calculations

Horsepower. By definition, horsepower is a measure of the rate at which work is done.

$$
\begin{aligned}
\text{One horsepower} &= 33{,}000 \text{ ft-lb/min} \\
&= 550 \text{ ft-lb/sec} \\
&= 746 \text{ watts (or } \tfrac{3}{4} \text{ kw)}
\end{aligned}
$$

Water horsepower. Water horsepower is the work required to lift a weight of water to a defined height per unit of time (usually a second or a minute). For the purpose of this field guide, friction is neglected.

$$
\text{Work} = \frac{\text{weight} \times \text{static height}}{\text{time}}
$$

For example: The work required to lift 10 lb of water one foot in one minute is as follows:

$$
\text{Work} = \frac{10 \text{ lb} \times 1 \text{ ft}}{1 \text{ min}} = 10 \text{ ft-lb/min}
$$

Water horsepower equals actual work per minute divided by 33,000 ft-lb per minute.

$$
\text{Water HP} = \frac{\text{work/min}}{33{,}000 \text{ ft-lb/min}}
$$

For pumps:

$$
\begin{aligned}
\text{Water HP} &= \frac{Q \text{ (gal/min)} \times 8.34 \text{ lb/gal} \times H \text{ (ft)}}{33{,}00 \, \dfrac{\text{ft/lb}}{\text{min}}} \\[2em]
&= \frac{Q \times 8.34 \times H \text{ (ft)}}{33{,}000 \, \dfrac{\text{ft-lb}}{\text{min}}}
\end{aligned}
$$

$$= \frac{Q \times 8.34 \times H}{33,000}$$

$$= \frac{QH}{3,957}$$

Rounded off:

Water horsepower $= \dfrac{Q \times H}{3,960}$

It should be noted that this equation is the one often used in operator certification tests.

Brake horsepower. Brake horsepower equals water horsepower divided by pump efficiency.

Pumps have inefficiencies as a result of water slippage, axial thrust in the volute, and routing the discharge water out. The actual horsepower required by the pump must take that inefficiency into account.

$$\text{Brake horsepower} = \frac{\text{water horsepower}}{\text{pump efficiency}}$$

Pump efficiency and brake horsepower are shown on the manufacturer's pump curves. Figure 1-3 illustrates a typical family of curves for a centrifugal pump with that information. Pump efficiency is already taken into account on the brake horsepower curves shown on this graph.

Actual horsepower. Actual horsepower equals brake horsepower divided by motor efficiency. New motors should have an electrical efficiency of 92 percent or greater. Older ones may be substantially less and should be considered for replacement. The electrical efficiency should be shown on the motor nameplate.

Motor Horsepower (Actual)

Motors do not operate at 100 percent efficiency. The actual motor horsepower required has to take motor efficiency into account (sometimes referred to as electrical efficiency).

(1,750 RPM)

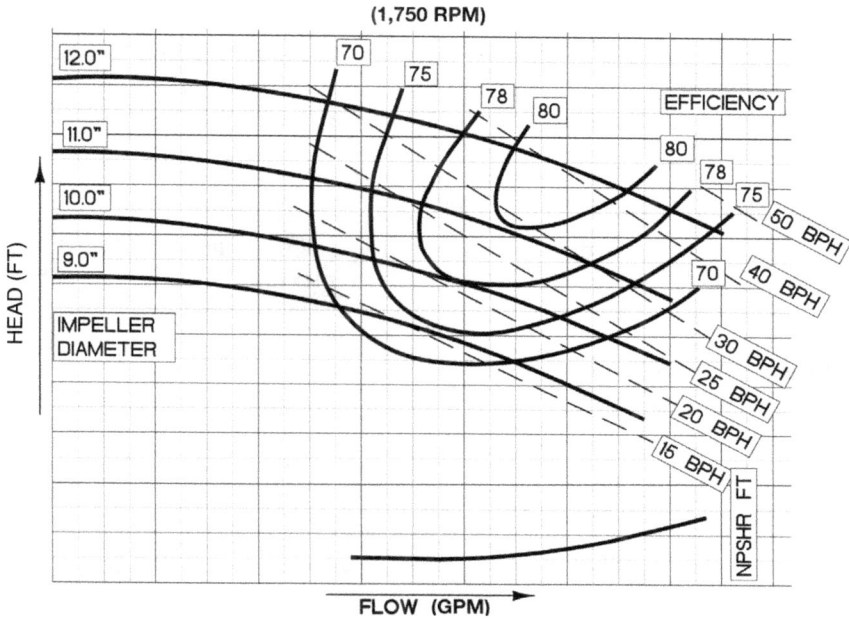

Figure 1-3   Typical centrifugal pump family of curves

$$\text{Motor horsepower (actual)} = \frac{\text{brake horsepower}}{\text{motor efficiency}}$$

$$= \frac{\text{water horsepower}}{\text{pump efficiency} \times \text{motor efficiency}}$$

Metric horsepower. Metric horsepower is not normally used in the United States. It is given for reference only.

$$\text{HP} = \frac{l \, / \, \min \times \text{H}}{3,905.74}$$

Where:
        HP = water horsepower
        l/min = liters per minute
        H = head, in meters
        3,905.74 = 3,960 × 0.9863*
* 1 cheval = 0.9863 or French horsepower

Example Problems

In the following section, a number of example problems are given for calculating horsepower and power usage. These problems are similar to those that might occur on an operator's certification test and do not include friction loss.

Example A:

A pump raises a flow of 60 gpm of water from level "A," with an elevation of 100 feet, to level "B," with an elevation of 210 feet. What is the horsepower being used?

Answer:

$$HP = \frac{Q \times H}{3{,}960}$$

$$Q = 60 \text{ gpm}$$

$$H = \underline{(210 \text{ ft} - 100 \text{ ft})}$$

$$= \frac{60 \times (210\text{-}100)}{3{,}960}$$

$$HP = 1.67$$

Is the answer in water horsepower, brake horsepower, or actual horsepower?

Answer:

Because no efficiencies are given, the answer is assumed to be in terms of water horsepower.

Example B:

If the pump and motor have a combined efficiency of 60 percent, how much actual horsepower would be used in the previous question?

Answer:

$$HP = \frac{\text{water horsepower}}{\text{motor efficiency} \times \text{pump efficiency}}$$

$$HP = \frac{1.67}{0.60} = 2.78 \text{ HP}$$

What motor size would be selected?

Answer:

The required motor size would be rounded up to 3 HP. Depending on the actual pump operating range, the motor used might be the next size up. (To be discussed in the next section.)

Example C:

Calculate the cost of power of the previous example.

Pumping Energy Costs:

Watts = HP × 746

kw = watts / 1,000

hr = hours of operation

kWh = kilowatts × hr

$$= \frac{746 \text{ HP} \times \text{hr}}{1,000}$$

TPC = kWh × unit cost of power

Calculate kilowatts.

$$\frac{2.78 \text{ HP} \times 746 \text{ watts/HP}}{1,000} = 2.07 \text{ kw}$$

Assume the cost of power to be $0.025 kWh

Operational Power Cost = 2.07 kw × $0.025 kWh

= $0.052/hr

Example D:

If electricity costs 2.5 cents per kWh, per above, what is the monthly cost if the pump in the previous two questions runs continuously?

Answer:

Calculate kilowatts.

Power used   = 2.07 kw (from previous)

Cost of Power = $0.052/hr (from previous) × 30 d × 24 hr/d

= $37.44/mo

Example E:

Calculate the pump efficiency using the power draw.

The power delivered by a motor is usually expressed in horsepower. Because one (1) horsepower equals 746 watts (or about ¾ of a kilowatt), the formula for efficiency becomes:

$$\% \text{ efficiency} = \frac{746 \times \text{HP}}{\text{watts input}} \times 100$$

For Example: If a motor uses 1,000 watts of power and delivers one (1) horsepower to a water pump, its efficiency is:

$$\text{Motor efficiency \%} = \frac{746 \text{ watts} \times 1 \text{ HP}}{1,000} \times 100$$

Motor efficiency   = 74.6%

Note: Does not include pump efficiency.

Summary

For on-site evaluation, it should not be necessary for O&M staff to calculate the horsepower of an existing facility. If problems occur during start-up, the designer should be consulted. However, the horsepower calculations should be available in an on-site manual for review if needed. The information contained in this section, plus that in the following sections, should help the O&M staff make their own evaluation. The evaluation by O&M staff will be especially important over time, as the pump ages. Also, any older motors should be included in the capital improvements plan and replaced as soon as practicable.

Another potential problem that could occur over time is the possibility of changed conditions in a system. Typical examples are increased demand and restructuring of a pressure zone. Should problems of any sort occur, design verification may be required. A summary of the design conditions should be available at each facility for that purpose.

Additional pump information and evaluation criteria are presented in the following sections of this handbook.

CHAPTER 2

Pump Types

Introduction

There are many types of pumps used in water and wastewater utility systems, treatment plants, and in commercial/industrial systems. Applications range from sewage pumps to ultra-clean industrial systems.

The key word is *systems*. A water system is a combination of pumps, valves, fittings, and piping designed to deliver water for many uses. Although there are portable pumps for specific purposes, most pumps are installed in permanent facilities. The function of pumps, as used in this discussion, is to increase flow and pressure to satisfy the needs of the system.

It is not the purpose of this handbook to discuss the operation of all the many types of pumps in use. Rather, the intent is to discuss the design and O&M requirements of several of the most common pump types. The principles involved in operation, design, and evaluation of these pumps can then be applied to others. Although O&M personnel may not be required to design a pump, the information contained in this handbook is intended to help personnel understand how a pump works and help in troubleshooting.

The goal for this chapter is to discuss sizing and to illustrate how to read and use the complete family of curves for a pump. Using this information, O&M staff should have the information necessary to determine the flow of a pump with a pressure gauge if it is operating properly and to also determine if it is not.

System Requirements

When sizing or selecting a pump, it is first necessary to determine the system requirements. As a minimum, a simple flow diagram should be developed, as shown in Figure 1-1. In this figure, Alternative A illustrates a pump with a suction lift, whereas Alternative B shows a flooded suction. In either case, the required pump pressure or head is calculated as the total static head from water surface to water surface, plus friction of the piping system, including valves, fittings, and flowmeters. Head is the pressure measured in feet or pounds per square inch (psi). The flow in gallons per minute (gpm) is determined by the needs of the system. Also, the total static head may vary, depending on the level in the receiving reservoir, and the level in the source water. The pump should be designed to operate at the maximum.

Net Positive Suction Head (NPSH)

Even in a *suction lift* system where the source water is lower than the pump, the pressure to the pump must be positive. However, suction pressure also includes atmospheric pressure, which must be considered in the design process. Therefore, atmospheric pressure at the site and potential variations must be taken into account. NPSH is described in Figure 2-1. A set of typical calculations for NPSH is shown in Figure 2-2. Although suction lift is allowed, it is recommended that

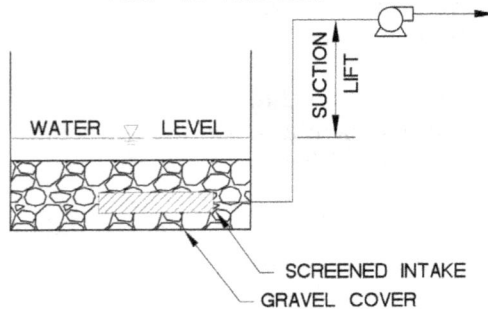

(NPSH) - THE ATMOSPHERIC PRESSURE AVAILABLE AT THE SUCTION WATER SURFACE.
(NPSHA) - THE TOTAL SUCTION PRESSURE AVAILABLE AT THE PUMP.
(NPSHR) - THE MINIMUM NPSH REQUIRED FOR THE PUMP TO FUNCTION

NOTES

1. THE NET POSITIVE SUCTION HEAD REQUIRED (NPSHR) IS A FUNCTION OF THE PUMP AND ITS OPERATING POINT. NPSHR MUST BE LESS THAN NPSHA FOR THE PUMP TO OPERATE. IF NPSHR BECOMES GREATER, THE PUMP WILL CAVITATE AND STOP PUMPING.

2. NOT NORMALLY A PROBLEM WITH POSITIVE SUCTION HEAD APPLICATIONS.

Figure 2-1   Net positive suction head (NPSH)

Net Positive Suction Head (NPSH)

The NPSH is the atmospheric pressure available at the water surface. For the purposes of this discussion, NPSHA is the available pressure at the pump suction. For a pump to function properly, there is a minimum NPSHR (required) which must be available. NPSHA is calculated as shown below.

$NPSHA = A - (V_p + V_H + H_f)$

Where:

$A =$ *Atmospheric pressure (ft)*
$V_p =$ *Vapor pressure of water (ft)*
$V_H =$ *Maximum velocity head (ft) in pipeline (should be as low as possible)*
$H_f =$ *Friction losses in intake pipeline (should be as low as possible)*

A typical NPSH calculation is shown below for the suction lift.

Assume: 1,000 ft elevation
75°F = Ambient temperature
$A =$ *32.8 ft*
$V_p =$ 0.84 ft
$V_H =$ *Assume negligible*
$H_f =$ *Assume 5 ft of piping and intake headloss and 10 ft of suction lift in the intake screen and support gravel.*

$$NPSH = \quad 32.8 - (0.84 - V_H^{\,0}) - H_{f1}\,(5\,ft) - H_{f2}\,(10\,ft)$$
$$= \quad 16.96\,ft$$

Figure 2-2   NPSH requirements

it be kept to a minimum. Even then, any fluctuation in suction side water level must be taken into account. If the suction side water level is reduced significantly, the pump flow rate may also need to be reduced. Information will be presented to demonstrate how to determine the operational limits of a pump, compared to its capability.

Suction side pressure. Pump systems are designed in many ways. Some pumps operate off of line pressure to boost the water to a different level. Others operate in wet wells or river intakes. A minimum suction side pressure of 20 psi is normally required for pumps operating off of line pressure. With pumps operating in river intakes or wet wells/sumps, the designer also has to take into account the physical sizing of the wet well or sump, which will be discussed further in this chapter.

Pump efficiency factors. In addition to satisfying system demands, it is also important to select a pump that is operating at or near its peak efficiency range if possible. The designer should be aware that impeller design and efficiency have changed in the last 20 years, so that newer designs are 5 to 10 percent more efficient. If the pump is that old, consideration may be given to replacing it.

Motor efficiency. There has also been a 5 to 10 percent increase in motor efficiency over the last 20 years. Motors with an efficiency of 94 percent or greater are available for centrifugal pumps. Submersible motors may have an efficiency in the range of 85 percent.

Replacement evaluation. An economic evaluation may be necessary to determine if a motor should be replaced or if the entire pump and motor assembly should be replaced. Initial capital costs, maintenance costs, and electrical power costs should be considered in a life cycle analysis to determine the most efficient and economical method of operating a system. Several economic models are available for a designer's use.

All of the items previously mentioned must be considered in the design and selection of a pump. The required flow and pressure (both suction and discharge) must be calculated to select a specific pump. Each of these subjects will be discussed in more detail in this handbook. Again, much of this information is presented as background to help O&M personnel better understand how to use pump curves.

Centrifugal Pump Types

Close coupled. Figure 2-3a illustrates a typical close coupled centrifugal pump. Close coupled means that the motor bolts directly to the pump volute, with no intermediate coupling, and the motor shaft connects to the impeller. A cutaway of the volute of a centrifugal pump is shown in the lower part of Figure 2-3a. The inlet flow comes into the eye (center) of the impeller, and as the impeller spins, it forces the water to the outside and increases both flow and pressure.

Vertical. Centrifugal pumps can be close coupled, as shown in Figure 2-3a, or in a vertical configuration, as shown in Figure 2-3b. In addition, larger pumps are often frame mounted, as shown on Figure 2-3c.

Frame mounted. A separate motor and pump configuration will allow either to be removed for maintenance without disturbing the other. However, the separation requires a coupling to connect the motor shaft to the pump shaft. Misalignment of the two can result in motor or pump failure, or both. A worn coupling could cause the same problems. Therefore, it is recommended that the pump and motor be properly aligned by a certified pump/motor technician.

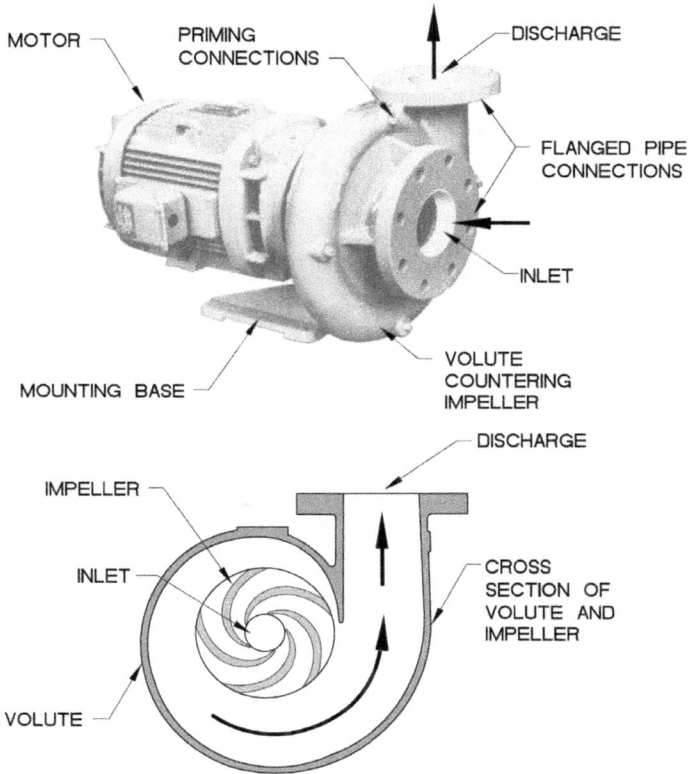

Figure 2-3a   Typical close coupled centrifugal pump

Family of curves. The operation of a specific centrifugal pump is illustrated by its *family of curves,* which is shown in Figure 1-3 (repeated in Chapter 4 as Figure 4-1). The typical family of curves includes impeller diameter, pump efficiency, brake horsepower, and net positive suction head required (NPSHR). For simplicity, this family of curves will be separated into its individual components and discussed further. It should be noted that each different pump will have its own individual family of curves. If one pump does not satisfy the requirements, another should be used.

1. Impeller curves. The impeller curves from Figure 2-4 are highlighted in Figure 2-5. The other sets of curves are included but are faded in the background so that the relationship between them can still be observed.

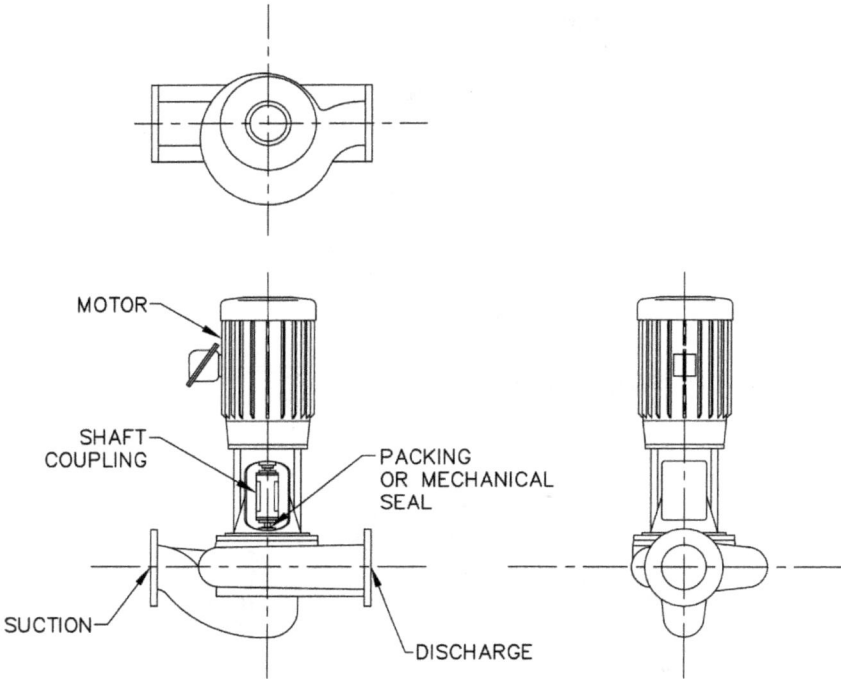

Figure 2-3b   Vertical centrifugal pump

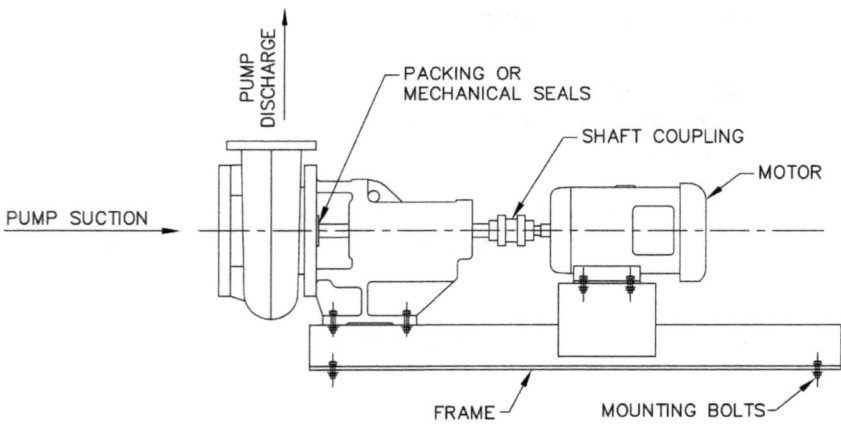

Figure 2-3c   Frame-mounted centrifugal pump

Referring again to Figure 2-3a, the impeller is illustrated in the cutaway drawing of the volute. In this case, the maximum impeller diameter is shown, which has the minimum clearance to the body of the volute. The maximum impeller diameter for this pump is shown as 12 in. in Figure 2-4, and the minimum is 9.0 in. The impeller can be trimmed anywhere between the two, to more closely match the desired operating conditions. Smaller-diameter impellers result in lower flow and pressure. Once an impeller diameter is selected, the pump will operate on that impeller curve without exception. Changing conditions will simply move the operating point left or right of its design point. If the system requires flow or pressure at a point below the impeller curve, a separate flow or pressure control valve, after the pump, must be used. Operating above the curve would require a larger impeller or a completely new pump.

Selecting a pump will be discussed in more detail later, but it is important to note that the smaller-diameter impellers create lower pump efficiencies because of increased slippage in the volute. If the efficiency becomes too low, it may be desirable to consider a different pump.

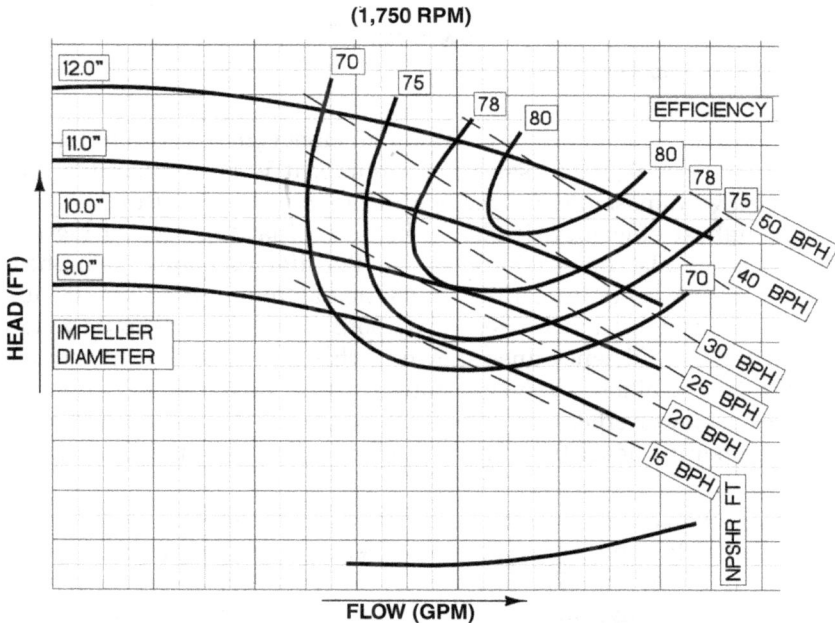

Figure 2-4   Typical centrifugal pump family of curves

(1,750 RPM)

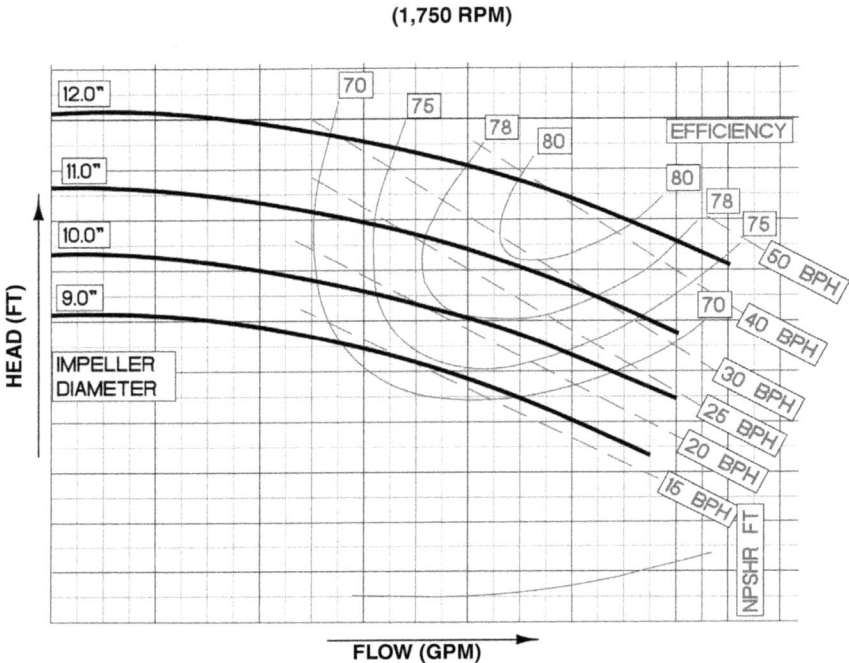

Figure 2-5   Impeller curves

2. Hydraulic efficiency. The hydraulic efficiency curves are highlighted in Figure 2-6. When selecting a pump, it is most desirable, but not always possible, for the operating point to be within the area of highest efficiency. It should be noted that the area of highest efficiency also has the largest impeller diameter and the highest horsepower requirements of a particular pump. Also, the design operating point and any secondary points of operation should all fall within the efficiency lines shown on this graph. Operating outside the lowest efficiency curves may result in unstable operation, as well as lower efficiency. If that is the case, a different pump, that can operate closer to its highest efficiency point may be required.

3. Brake horsepower. Water horsepower is that which is required to actually lift the water. Brake horsepower is the power required to rotate the impeller at a given flow rate and pressure, taking into account hydraulic inefficiencies of the pump. The term itself refers to the power required to *brake* or stop the impeller. It is the water horsepower divided by the pump efficiency. The pump

(1,750 RPM)

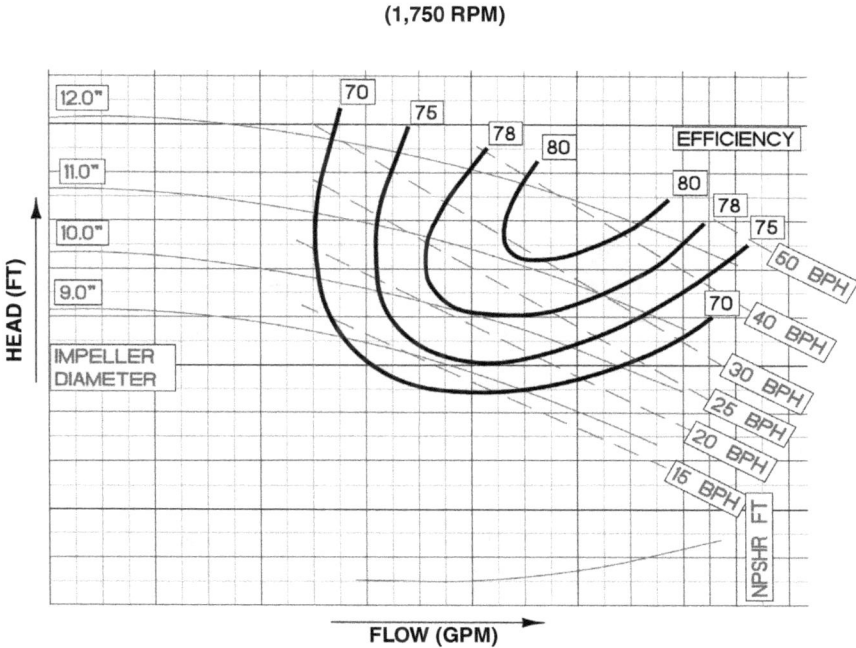

Figure 2-6   Hydraulic efficiency curves

efficiency has already been considered in Figure 2-4 to show the power requirements.

As shown on Figure 2-4 and highlighted on Figure 2-7, the brake horsepower curves are not parallel with the various impeller curves. In fact, brake horsepower curves cross over the impeller curves. As shown in these figures, the horsepower requirements increase as the flow increases and as the operating point travels to the right on the impeller curve. The motor horsepower should be adequate for the higher flow rates, if a pump has more than one operating point (which is common). In fact, it is recommended that the motor be large enough for any point on the impeller curve (nonoverloading across the range).

4. Net positive suction head required (NPSHR). The curve for NPSHR is highlighted on Figure 2-8. Although the term *suction head* is used, a pump always needs positive suction pressure (including atmospheric), as discussed previously. It is important to note that the NPSHR increases significantly as the flow increases.

(1,750 RPM)

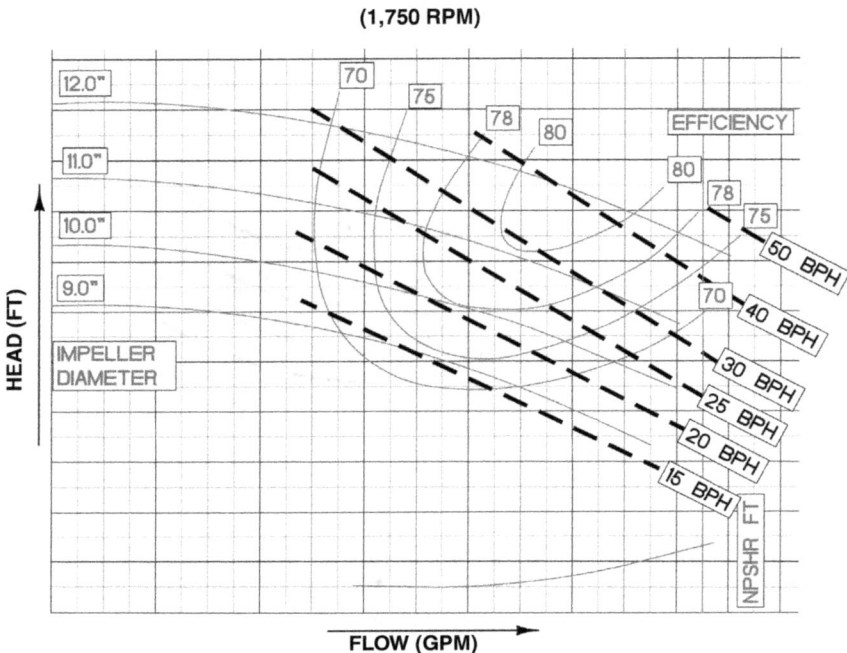

Figure 2-7   Brake horsepower curves

It is not recommended for a pump to operate far to the right on its impeller curve. The horsepower required can increase and the NPSHR can more than double, as shown on Figure 2-8. Therefore, it is recommended that flow controls be provided for any pump operating with a suction lift to prevent it from exceeding its operating limits.

To actually operate to the right of the impeller curve, a larger motor may be required, along with more positive suction pressure. To that end, every effort should be made to reduce head loss on the suction side, including the use of large pipe with no restrictions. Also, the design conditions in the recommended on-site O&M manual should be reviewed to ensure that the pump is operating within its limits.

Centrifugal Pump Selection

When selecting a pump, the primary factors used are the required flow rate, the discharge pressure, and the type of service. The flow is determined from the system requirements, and the pressure is the combination of static head and pressure loss (head loss) caused by

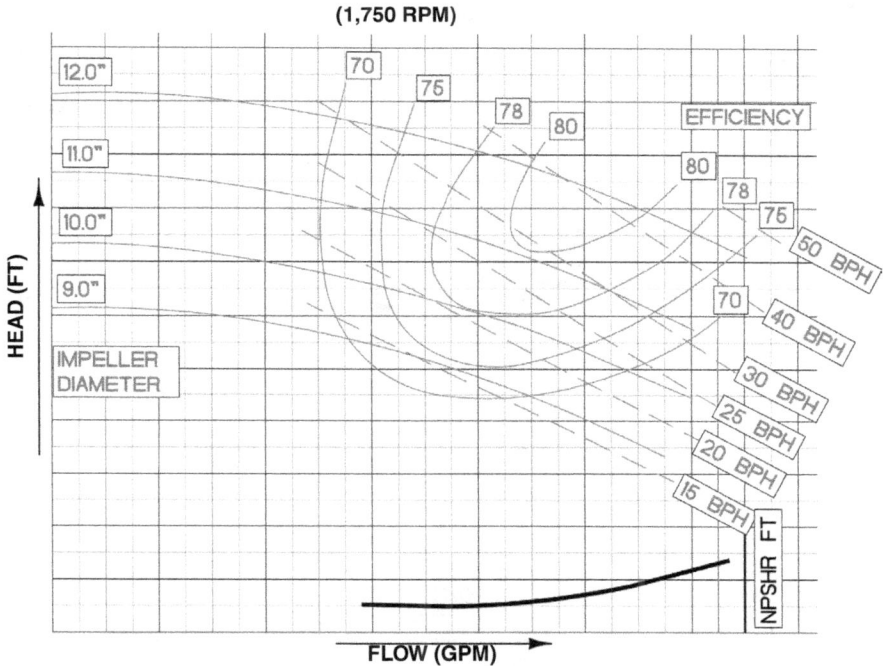

Figure 2-8   Net positive suction head curve

piping, valves, fittings, etc. The type of service includes the location of the pump with regard to the source water (flooded suction, mounted over a sump, etc.) and the type of source water (clean, dirty raw water, or high-solids wastewater). Once these factors are known, the pump can be selected using the family of curves for various pumps, such as has been shown in the previous figures.

Efficiency

The most desirable operating point would be within that part of the curve containing the highest efficiency. If the pump can operate within or near that high-efficiency zone, that particular pump would be a good selection. (Figure 2-9.)

Motor Size

Brake horsepower. The design point will often fall in between two impeller curves, as shown on Figure 2-9. For those cases, the impeller can be trimmed from the larger size to coincide with the design

(1,750 RPM)

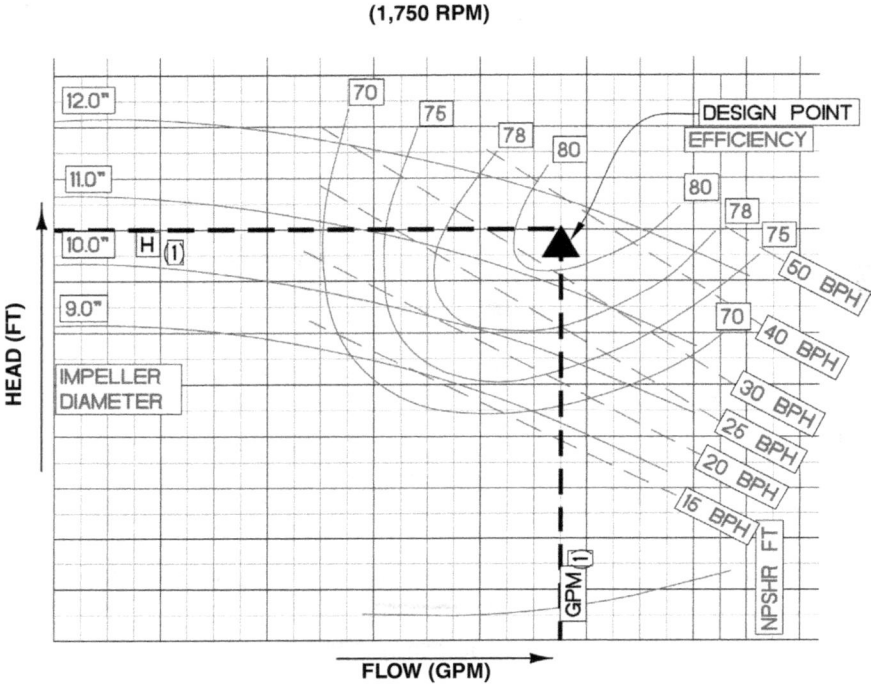

Figure 2-9   Proposed design efficiency

point. The impeller curve resulting from the changed diameter will be parallel to and in between the smaller and larger impeller sizes on either side of the design point.

Using the design point and the new impeller size, a new impeller curve can be extended left and right of the design point to determine the required motor size. Once an impeller is selected, the pump must operate on that curve because of the physical constraints of the pump. If the pump is throttled back, the operating point will travel to the left on the impeller curve. If the pump is allowed to run faster, the operating point will travel to the right of the design point on the impeller curve.

It should be noted that the horsepower shown on the previous figures refers to *brake horsepower*. (Refer to Chapter 1.) Brake horsepower already takes into account the efficiency of the pump, as shown on the graph, but does not take into account the electrical motor efficiency. True motor horsepower may be 6 to 8 percent higher than shown in these figures, or more, depending on its age. Even then, the required motor horsepower will usually have to be rounded to the next higher size to account for a performance factor (conservative design factor) and to reach a value that is commercially available.

Nonoverloading across the range. The configuration of many pump systems often results in variations in flow from the design point. Moving the pump to the right increases flow, reduces pressure, increases the NPDES, and increases the horsepower required. As stated previously, the impeller and horsepower curves are not parallel (Figure 2-7). Moving the operating point to the right often results in the impeller curve crossing over a horsepower curve. In such cases, a smaller motor would overheat and likely fail. To avoid that condition, the motor can be sized to be adequate for any reasonable condition on the impeller curve. The term *reasonable* refers to the area within the family of curves. Sizing the motor using this method is referred to by the author as *nonoverloading across the range,* and is recommended method.

Using the nonoverloading method of selecting a motor is only valid when the operating point is still within its family of curves. Operating a centrifugal pump too far to the right or in an unrestricted condition (wide open) will likely result in damage to the pump and/ or the motor regardless. It is then too far out of the normal operating range to be considered in design or motor selection. Flow or pressure controls, or both, are recommended to stop the pump if it begins to operate too far off the design point.

Pump Curve Shape

Once a pump has been selected, it will operate along its impeller curve, as discussed previously. Figure 2-10 represents a fixed impeller size. The pressure produced is $H_{(1)}$ with a flow of $GPM_{(1)}$. For discussion purposes, the pump motor is assumed to operate at 1,750 rpm.

Having selected a pump based on the design information discussed previously does not mean that it is the proper pump for a specific application. Pumps are often used to operate away from the design point by either throttling back to a lower flow or reducing pressure and allowing them to run at a higher flow rate. In that case, the shape of the impeller curve may have a significant impact on the suitability of the pump to operate within the requirements of a particular system. For example, in Figure 2-11, curves are shown that are both shallower and steeper than the typical pump curve selected previously. At this point, it is for the designer to determine the effect on the system of the shape of the curve.

Normally, pump selection is relatively easy. However, there have been many cases where the author has had to give extensive

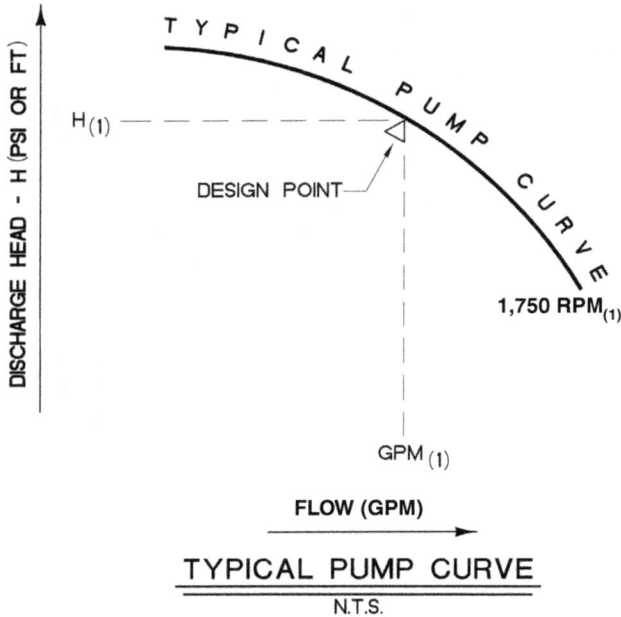

TYPICAL PUMP CURVE

N.T.S.

NOTE

THE TYPICAL PUMP CURVE REPRESENTS THE
SELECTION OF A SPECIFIC IMPELLER

Figure 2-10   Pump selection, operation, and variable-frequency drives

consideration to the shape of the curve. For example, if the pump is
producing a high pressure and has a steep curve, changing the flow
rate would have the impact of changing the pressure dramatically.
On the other hand, changing the pressure on a pump with a shallow
curve would have a similar impact on the flow. Raising the pressure
significantly in a potable water distribution system could cause
problems with water heaters in individual residences with a steep
impeller curve. Therefore, the shape of the curve may dictate the type
of pump being used and is an important consideration for the designer.
It is recommended that the O&M personnel evaluate the system effects
on the pump and determine if the pump is an acceptable selection.

Pressure/Flow Relationship

Once an impeller size has been selected for a specific pump, the
pump must operate on its impeller curve as discussed previously.

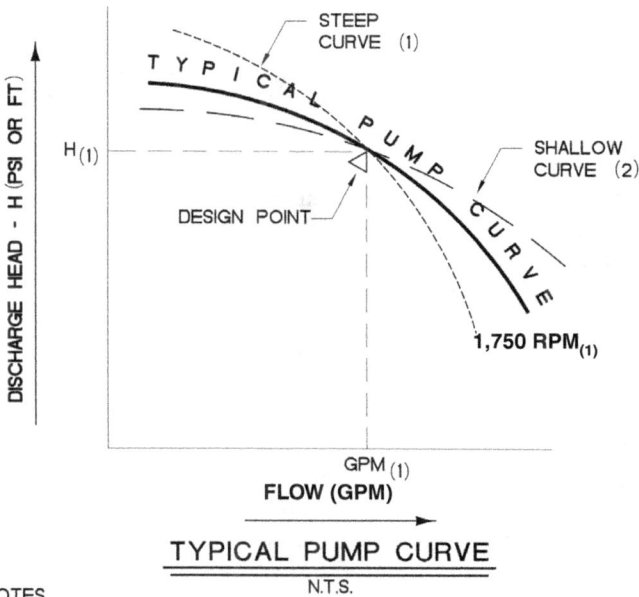

DISCHARGE HEAD - H (PSI OR FT)

FLOW (GPM)

STEEP CURVE (1)

TYPICAL PUMP CURVE

SHALLOW CURVE (2)

H(1)

DESIGN POINT

1,750 RPM(1)

GPM (1)

TYPICAL PUMP CURVE
N.T.S.

NOTES

1. A STEEP CURVE WILL CAUSE RAPID CHANGES IN PRESSURE WITH ANY CHANGE IN FLOW.

2. A SHALLOW CURVE WILL CAUSE RAPID CHANGES IN FLOW WITH ANY CHANGE IN PRESSURE.

Figure 2-11   Centrifugal pump curve shape

Therefore, for any discharge pressure in its operating range, the pump will produce a specific flow as indicated in Figure 2-10. Using that relationship, O&M personnel can easily determine if a pump is operating properly, which will be discussed in more detail.

Pressure Boost

The pressure produced by a pump, as indicated by its impeller curve, is the pressure boost generated *above* the pressure of the inlet of the pump. The actual pump discharge pressure will be the pressure boost above the suction side system pressure.

Vertical Line Shaft Turbine Pumps

A typical vertical line shaft turbine pump is shown in Figure 2-12. This pump has the motor installed vertically on top of the discharge head, all of which is above grade on a floor or on a raised pad. A pipe column is extended down beneath the motor into the pump well, as shown. A shaft is extended from the motor down through the pipe column to the impellers, and the pumped water flows upward in the column past the shaft.

Depending on the depth of the well or sump, there may be one or more sections of shafting and pipe columns. The pipe column has internal bushings at each joint to keep the shaft in alignment. One or more impeller assemblies may be installed on the bottom, with an intake screen (if used).

Multiple impellers are often used to increase the discharge pressure. It is common for pump curves to only show the characteristics of a single impeller. The actual discharge pressure is then a multiplication of the value from the impeller curve times the number of impellers. It is important that the number of impellers be indicated in the on-site O&M documentation.

These pumps are commonly used for potable water in below-grade sumps, for deep groundwater wells, and in other applications. In the case of deep wells, there are multiple sections of shafting and pump column. The manufacturer should be consulted for a recommendation of the desired length of sections. It should be noted that shorter sections are usually desired to help keep the shaft straight, as discussed in the following section.

There are several important considerations in the design of a vertical line shaft turbine pump.

Minimum Submergence

For this type of pump, the submergence is the height of water above the inlet bell, as shown in Figure 2-12. If the water level is drawn down below a minimum level, the rotation of the pump could induce a vortex on the surface of the water, thereby inducting air into the pump and causing an unstable operation. Therefore, it is very important to calculate the usable volume of a pump well as being the amount of water above that minimum level. Level controls should be provided to start the pump at a high level and to stop it before a minimum level is reached. In some cases, a deeper pit may be needed underneath the pump to allow the pump column and impellers to be extended down to a lower level than the rest of the pump well, thereby increasing the submergence. An inspection of the water surface in the sump will indicate if there is a problem.

Minimum Height

The rule of thumb for this type of pump is for the inlet bell to be at least half the diameter above the bottom of the sump. The intent

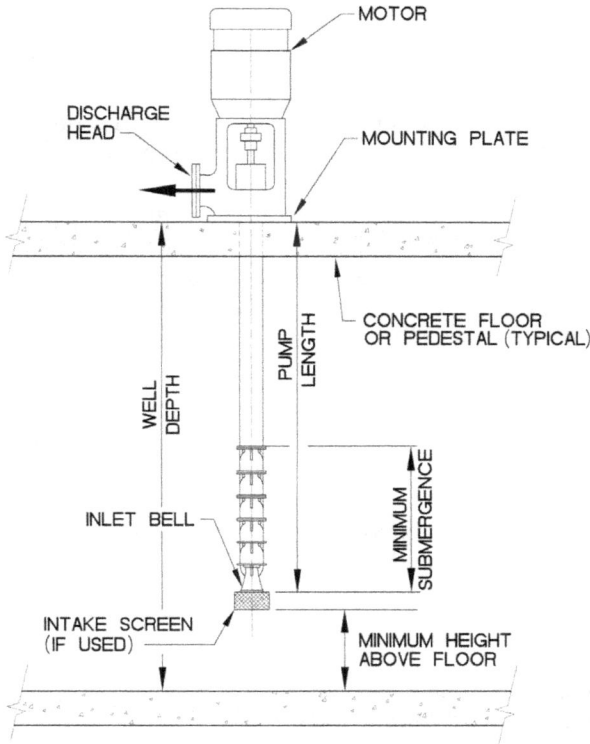

Figure 2-12   Typical vertical line shaft turbine pump

is to prevent any restrictions on the suction side. However, it is recommended that the height be equal to the diameter of the pump for a conservative design. Too low a clearance could result in increased suction head loss and unstable operation.

Water Quality

A vertical line shaft turbine pump is generally intended for relatively clean water. Using this pump for high solids or water containing high amounts of sand or grit is not recommended by the author. The water being pumped has to pass upward through the pipe column, past the shaft bushings, to the discharge head. Grit and sand can cause very high wear on the bushings, resulting in shaft wobble, unstable operation, and ultimate pump failure. When there is no other good choice of pump, some effort should be made to keep the sand and grit out of the well and away from the pump.

Intake Screen

Figure 2-12 shows an intake screen on the bottom of the suction bell of the pump. As stated previously, vertical line shaft turbine pumps may not be the best selection where there are high solids of any type. If an intake screen were to collect solids and become fouled, it could affect the operation of the pump, and there is no easy way for it to be cleaned. Either a diver would have to be sent into the wet well or the entire pump would have to be pulled for cleaning. If it is not cleaned, additional solids could pass underneath and enter the pump, and could cause higher suction head loss and unstable operation. Because of these difficulties, the designer or owner may choose not to include an intake screen.

Pump Mounting

Figure 2-12 shows the motor and discharge head mounted directly to a concrete floor. Because of the weight of the pump assembly, and the torque of the motor, considerable reinforcing may be required in the concrete. For that purpose, a concrete pedestal is usually provided to spread the weight of the pump and motor, and to provide suitable anchorage.

Starter

It may seem obvious to most, but a slow-start starter should be provided for any large pump motor. The author has observed cases where the concrete pedestal supporting the pump was coming apart because of the force generated by a large motor being started rapidly with an across-the-line starter. Starting slowly also provides a level of protection to the pump itself from damage.

Packing/Mechanical Seals

Either packing or a mechanical seal is used to seal the shaft in the discharge head. If packing is used, some amount of leakage will be expected. In that case, tubing should be attached to the discharge head to allow drainage to the nearest drain.

If mechanical seals or bearings are used, it is recommended that a supply of fresh water be connected to the discharge head for flushing purposes to help keep the bearings and seals clean. The author inspected one line-shaft vertical turbine pump used in a deep well that used vegetable oil for lubrication. Over a period of years, enough oil had leaked into the well to completely foul the casing. Another pump was vibrating badly because of grit in the water, which caused excessive bushing and shaft wear.

Bearing failure constitutes a large percentage of pump failures. Therefore, proper design and maintenance are critical to pump and motor life. Vibration in the pump head or motor could be an indication of a bearing or seal failure, as well as unstable operation.

Shaft Height Adjustment

The proper shaft length is critical to the operation of the impellers. Adjusting the shaft length positions the impellers properly with respect to the volute. The various impellers and bowl assemblies are bolted together and connected to the shaft at the bottom of the pump column, as shown in Figure 2-13. Clearances between the impeller and the volute are critical for proper operation and to prevent undue wear. It is recommended that the shaft length be adjusted by pump technicians, because they should have the proper tools, equipment, and training for the purpose. If the height has not been checked in some time, it is recommended that it be scheduled.

Optimum Operating Range

The solid lines in Figure 2-14 represent an operating or impeller curve for an actual vertical line shaft turbine pump. In the middle of the graph, there is an area where the curve changes slope to become nearly horizontal, and then changes slope again to continue downward. A change in slope of this type is called an inflection. Within this area or zone, there is little or no change in pressure for any change in flow rate. Operating within this zone then creates an unstable condition where the pump can jump from one flow rate to another with no external changes. Flow control in that zone is extremely difficult, if not impossible. As shown in Figure 2-13, the water can come in one side of the pump inlet bell and

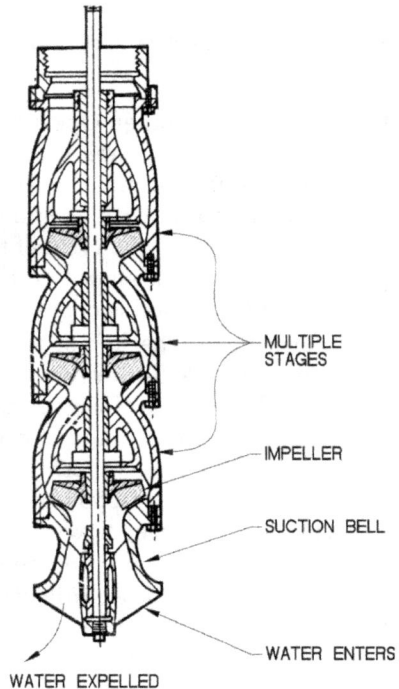

MULTIPLE STAGES

IMPELLER

SUCTION BELL

WATER ENTERS

WATER EXPELLED

Figure 2-13   Unstable operation

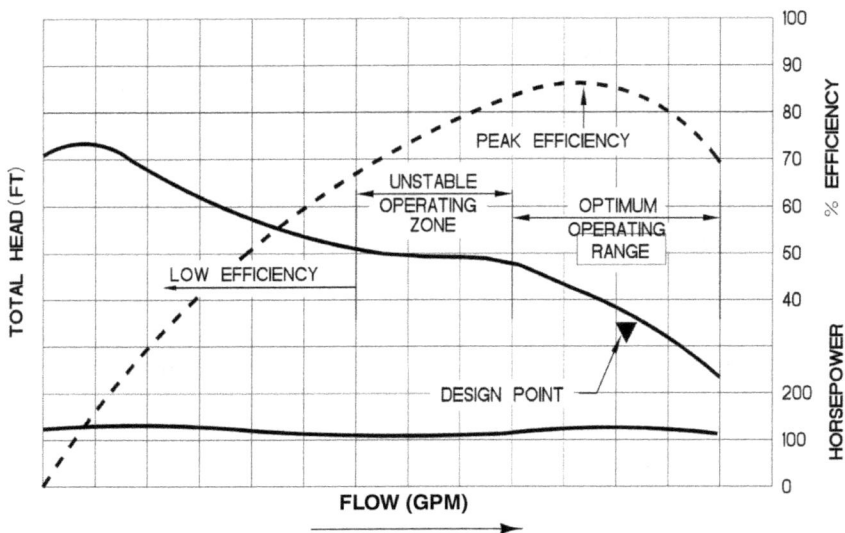

Figure 2-14   Typical vertical turbine pump curve

be thrown out the other. Operating in this manner will cause the entire pump assembly to vibrate, which in turn will cause accelerated wear to the shaft, shaft bushings, bearings, and the inlet bell. Therefore, when a pump has a curve with an inflection zone such as this, it is highly desirable to operate to the right of that part of the curve. In this case, the peak efficiency point shown on the dotted line in Figure 2-14 is also to the right of the unstable operating zone.

Operating to the left of the inflection zone is not recommended either because of the very low efficiency. Referring to the horsepower curve on the bottom of Figure 2-14, it can be seen that the power requirements for this pump vary only a small amount from one location to another. Therefore, operating at a higher flow rate is again desirable, because the horsepower requirements are the same at a higher flow rate as at a lower flow rate.

In a manufacturer's literature, the standard operating curves may not show as dramatic an inflection point as is depicted in Figure 2-14. However, it is still best to pick an operating point to the right of those areas. It is recommended that the owner or designer selecting a large pump of this type request the manufacturer to provide an actual test on the pump to develop an accurate curve. Any unstable operating zone may then be better defined.

Submersible Pumps

There are two different types of pumps that can be called a submersible type: a solids-handling pump, as shown in Figure 2-15, and a deep well type, shown in Figure 2-16. Solids handling pumps are less common than other types in potable water systems. However, they are often found in waste handling systems in water treatment plants and in raw water intakes for removal of accumulated sand, grit, and dirt.

Solids Handling Pumps

A cutaway of a large submersible solids-handling pump is shown in Figure 2-15. The intake comes from below and the discharge is directed toward the left and into a piping system. Pumps of this type are, of necessity, hermetically sealed to prevent the entrance of moisture. The power wiring is also sealed where it enters the pump motor on the upper right of this figure.

Efficiency. A problem in the design of these types of submersible pumps is the dissipation of heat in a sealed compartment. As a result, their pump motors are generally less efficient than a comparable centrifugal pump, although improvements have been made. The open impeller common for solids handling also makes the pump portion of the assembly somewhat less efficient than a centrifugal type with a closed impeller. A typical family of curves for a solids-handling submersible pump is shown in Figure 2-17.

Motor alarms. Several different types of alarms are usually included with this type of pump that are not provided on others. The alarms indicate overheating and the presence of moisture. In the author's opinion, these alarms are essential in

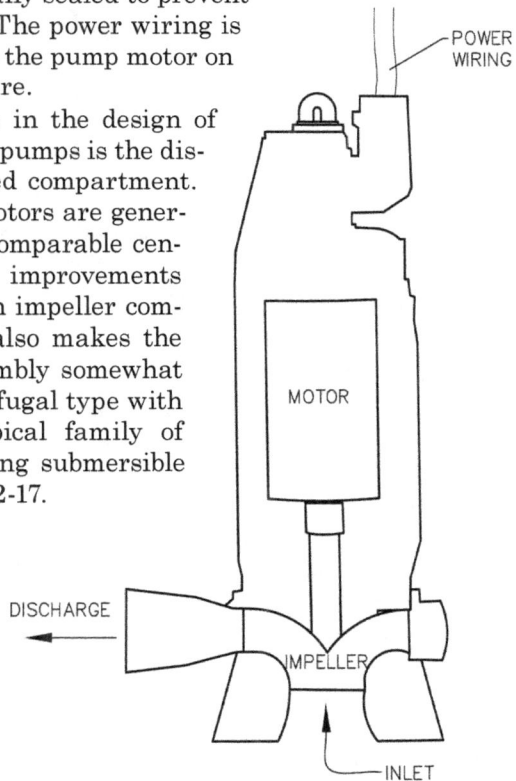

Figure 2-15   Typical submersible pump cross section

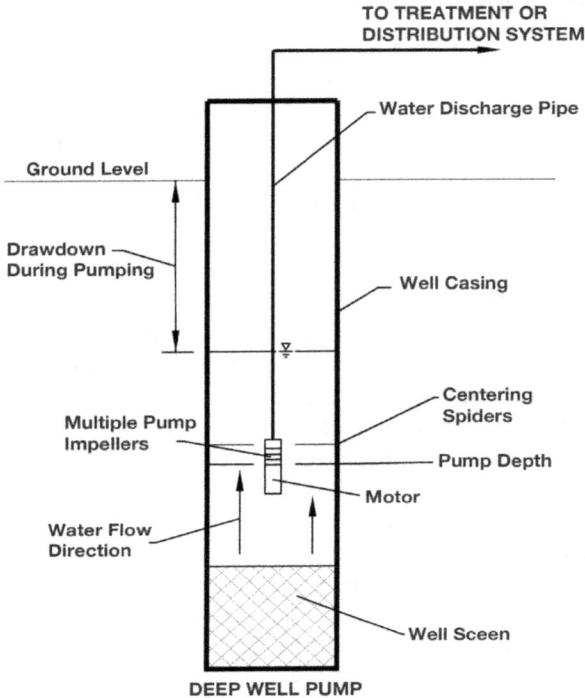

TO TREATMENT OR DISTRIBUTION SYSTEM

Water Discharge Pipe

Ground Level

Drawdown During Pumping

Well Casing

Centering Spiders

Multiple Pump Impellers

Pump Depth

Motor

Water Flow Direction

Well Sceen

DEEP WELL PUMP

Figure 2-16   Deep well submersible pump

any submersible pump installation. An early warning may prevent what otherwise might be a total failure. It is recommended that the O&M personnel verify that these alarms are present and that they are properly monitored by the control system.

Submersible pump motors are very susceptible to moisture damage. The author is aware of one installation where the power cable was left loose on the pump well floor, during construction, and became submerged for several hours. Water wicked up the wiring during that period and ruined the motor before it was placed in operation (twice).

Installation. Submersible solids handling pumps can be installed in several ways, including being lowered into a basin by a cable from the lifting loop on top, as shown in Figure 2-18. Pumps of that type may also use flexible piping for the pump discharge. Several different types of installations of submersible pumps are shown in Figure 2-18, including cable lift on the right, a permanent assembly in the center, and a

(—) Hydraulic End Efficiency (%)   (—·—) Power Limits

NO CONTINUOUS OPERATION
IN DASHED AREA

100 HP

HEAD (FT)

FLOW (GPM)

NPSHre (FT)

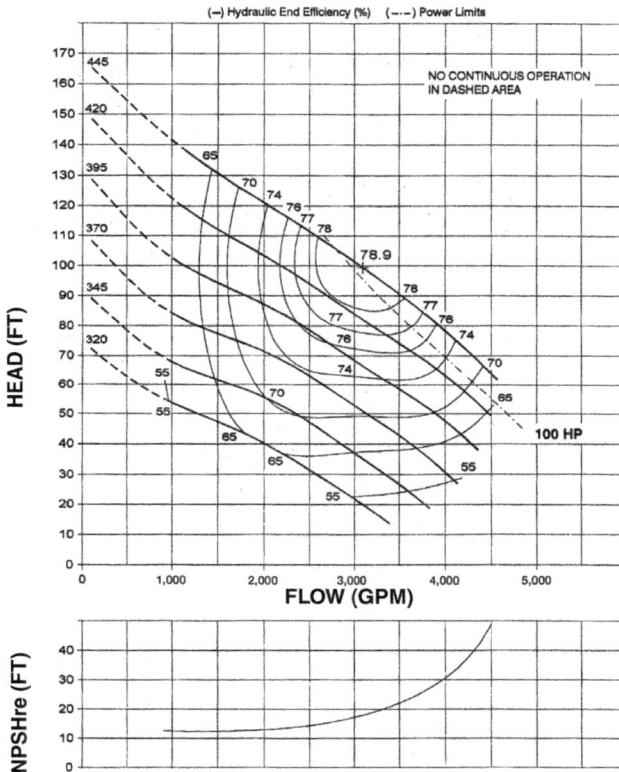

NOTE: Curves are based on nominal constant hydraulic-end speed and show performance with clear water.

Figure 2-17   Typical submersible pump curve

rail type with a quick-connect piping system on the left. Using the quick disconnect and rail system, the pump is lowered by a cable and slides down a pair of rails. At the bottom, the effluent connection slides into a quick disconnect/connect assembly, which allows the use of fixed rigid effluent piping. A duplex installation of solids-handling pumps with a quick connect/disconnect rail system is shown in Figure 2-19.

Wet well design. When designing a wet well for any type pump, it is important that the approach velocity of the water to the pump not be high. It is also important that the incoming water approach the pump in a smooth fashion without creating turbulence close to the pump. A smooth and uniform approach is very important to pump operation.

In the design of a wet well or sump, there are a number of other factors to consider, including system demand, wet well volume, area,

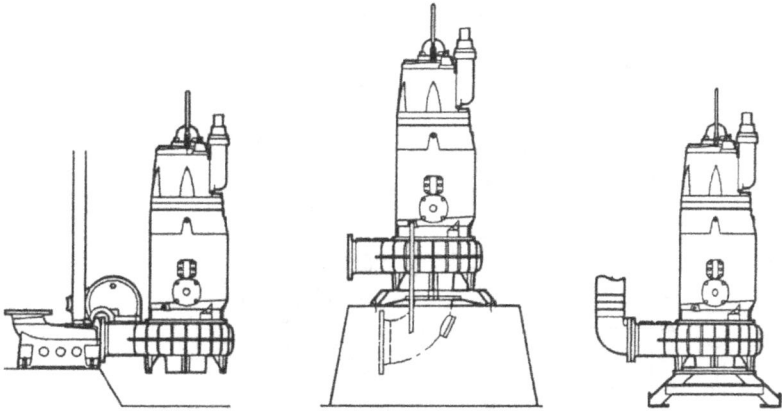

Figure 2-18   Typical submersible pump installation

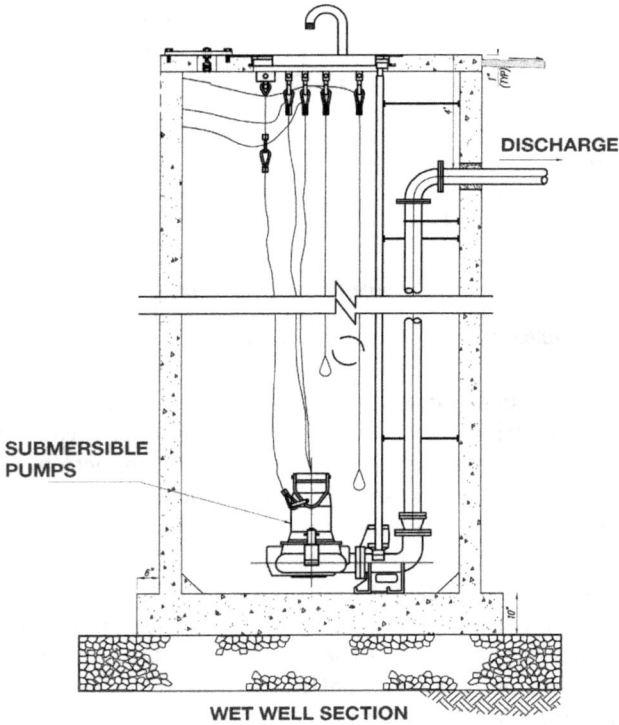

Figure 2-19   Duplex unit with valve box

depth, and the number of pumps. The designer must configure volume, area, and depth to limit the number of pump starts and stops per hour. An important factor in all pumping systems is the system demand. For example, consider a stormwater wet well that has very high flow for short periods of time and low flow most of the time. The pumps must be capable of handling the peak flow. However, if the average or normal flow is less than the design peak, the pumps may stop and start too often. Frequent starting and stopping can be mitigated by having smaller pumps in addition to the large pump and having a large enough wet well capacity. The system demand must be determined before the pumping system and wet well can be designed. Predesigned wet well systems are available. However, the designer must make sure that any standard design used meets all the system demand conditions under consideration.

Deep well pumps. An illustration of a deep well pump was shown in Figure 2-16. The configuration of this pump is different than the other, where the motor is on the bottom, with the impellers above, and the entire assembly is suspended from the discharge piping. One of the characteristics of this type of pump is that an upward flow of water past the motor is needed to provide cooling. As a result, the pump is normally installed above the well screens and well below the maximum drawdown level.

Centering

The power wiring and a level control cable are typically strapped to the pipe of a submersible pump to keep them in place. In addition, centering spiders are used to keep a deep well pump assembly in the middle of the well pipe and to prevent the motor from swinging over on the end of the discharge piping and contacting the well casing. If that were to occur, cooling would be prevented in that area, and it is possible for the motor to easily burn out. The author has witnessed a case where that occurred, and a burn spot was visible on the motor housing where contact was made with the well casing.

Drawdown

A major factor in the placement of a deep well pump is the drawdown experienced while the pump is operating. Depending on the soil conditions at a particular site, the well casing may penetrate through several different aquifers to reach the intended water-bearing zone. The static water level for a particular water-bearing zone often varies dramatically from one site to another. Some aquifers may be artesian, wherein a pump is not necessary for the water to flow out the top of the well. Even in such cases, a pump may be required to achieve the desired discharge pressure.

In most cases, the static water level for a given aquifer will be some distance below ground level. Then when the pump is operating, the water level will be drawn down further, depending on the transmissivity of the soil type in that particular aquifer. The static water level, the amount of drawdown at the design flow rate, and the recovery time should all be determined by a pump test on a pilot well prior to the design or construction of a large well. For a small well, these factors may be determined after the production well is drilled.

The pump and motor assembly should be installed at a depth far enough below the anticipated drawdown level to prevent vortexing. The manufacturer should be consulted for a recommended depth.

Level Controls

Level controls need to be configured for a well pump to prevent the water being drawn down far enough to cause problems or to interfere with pump operations. If the pump is shut off for low water level, a period of time should be allowed for the water level to recover before the pump is turned on again. The recovery may be achieved by allowing a period of time to elapse, or a level control can be activated to automatically turn the pump back on when the desired static water level is reached.

Each different deep well submersible pump will have its own family of curves, like the others mentioned in this handbook. It should be noted that the pump should be designed to lift water from the lowest drawdown point to the highest receiving water level. Adequate horsepower and impeller assemblies should be provided for that purpose. It should also be noted that a typical family of curves will show a discharge pressure for one set of impellers. Multiple impellers are normally required to produce the desired discharge pressure from a deep well pump.

Estimating Performance

One of the goals of this section is to illustrate how to estimate the performance of pumps while operating. The primary performance factors of a pump are the flow rate and the boost in pressure it provides.

Ideally, a pump installation would have an effluent flowmeter and pressure gauges on the suction and discharge sides of the pump.

The original design calculations and pressure boost should be available in an O&M manual on site for reference. Once the pressure boost is known, the resulting flow can be easily determined. Using the pressure boost (discharge pressure – suction pressure), the flow rate can be determined by using the pump impeller curve as shown in Figure 2-10. If the pump is operating properly, the pressure boost should be as designed, and the measured flow (from a flowmeter or rise rate calculations) should be equal to the value obtained from the impeller curve.

The discharge pressure reading can be used to determine if the pump is operating as intended. A lower than normal pressure might indicate a high flow, which could be caused by a leak in the distribution system, or it could be caused by excessive pump wear or bearing failure. On the other hand, a higher than normal pressure could be caused by a partially closed valve or other obstruction. Both high pressure and high flow, above the design point, are not possible at the same time. However, low pressure or low flow indicates either a problem with the pump, or a piping failure, and should be investigated.

Even if the flow is not known, the discharge pressure is easily checked and should always be consistent. If not, the O&M personnel should evaluate the entire system for potential problems.

Pressure Gauges

Because pumps represent a large capital expense, as well as an operating expense, the accessories should be reliable and of high quality. In the author's opinion, pressure gauges are an example of a small additional expense resulting in a large benefit. The author has observed many installations where troubleshooting was difficult because of unreliable pressure gauges.

Oil-filled gauges with a stainless steel case are recommended. In addition, large dials are recommended (3½-in. diameter) with scales large enough to read small changes in pressure. It should be noted that in a suction lift situation, a combination pressure/vacuum gauge may be required on the suction side of the pump.

A ¼-in. gauge cock-type shutoff valve is also recommended to easily install or remove a gauge.

Pressure Gauge Location

The discharge velocity from a pump is usually higher than desired for a piping system. Therefore, an increase in pipe size along with an isolation valve and a check valve are often just downstream from a pump. It is recommended that pressure gauges be installed on the larger piping, at least several diameters downstream for more accurate readings, as shown in Figure 2-20. High pipe velocity and turbulence can make pressure gauge readings *bounce* and reduce accuracy.

The information in this chapter is provided to demonstrate simple methods that can be used by O&M personnel to quickly determine if a pump is operating properly. The design flow, pressure boost, and impeller curves should be included in an on-site O&M manual to assist in their evaluation. Additional operational information is included in the following chapters.

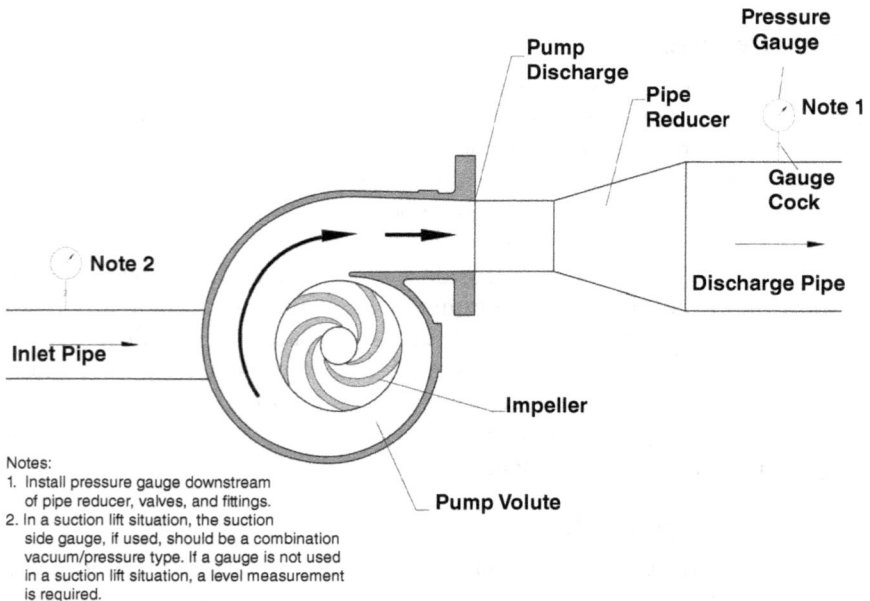

Notes:
1. Install pressure gauge downstream of pipe reducer, valves, and fittings.
2. In a suction lift situation, the suction side gauge, if used, should be a combination vacuum/pressure type. If a gauge is not used in a suction lift situation, a level measurement is required.

Figure 2-20   Pressure gauge installation

CHAPTER 3

Flow Variations

Introduction

Pump Operation

Pumps are intended to function according to the system needs. Many pumps are configured to simply turn on and off based on level control in a receiving reservoir, as shown in Figure 1-1. On the other hand, there are many pumping systems that require that the pump discharge rate be regulated or modified to meet the changing demands of the system. To satisfy such a demand, the pump discharge rate can be modulated using a rate control valve, or a variable-speed-drive motor can be provided to change the pump speed and therefore the flow rate.

Redundancy

Water systems are often designed and constructed based on a well-defined budget. In those cases, it may be difficult to provide a high level of redundancy. If that is the case, it is recommended that space be left for at least one other pump that could be provided in the future. Whether for satisfying system demand or providing backup, multiple pumps are desirable to maintain system capability.

Sizing Strategies

There are a number of strategies that can be used to size a pump based on percent demand, the size of the system, redundancy required, and economics. A variable demand can also be satisfied by multiple pumps.

1. One pump at 100 percent capacity could be provided, especially in a small system. However, one pump has no redundancy.

2. Two pumps at 100 percent could be provided, which would give redundancy. One pump could be operated at a time, and the two pumps alternated for increased life.

3. Two pumps at 50 percent capacity would provide a level of redundancy if one were to fail.

4. Three pumps at 50 percent capacity would provide one complete unit for redundancy.

5. Three pumps at one-third capacity would provide two-thirds redundancy if one were to fail. Three pumps also provide an amount of flow variation of one-third, two-thirds, or 100 percent capacity.

If three pumps are provided, the author's preference is to size one at 50 percent capacity and the other two at 25 percent capacity. In this way, there is at least 50 percent redundancy if the large unit fails, whereas four different operating conditions are provided at 25, 50, 75, and 100 percent.

Multiple Pumps

A larger system may have multiple pumps of different sizes. However, the number and sizing of the pumps is always dependent on the system needs and any variable demand that has to be met by the pumps. Therefore, when expanding a system or adding pumps, it is recommended that a computer model be generated to predict the best sizing strategy. With multiple pumps, one may have a flow control valve to allow it to be throttled up or down slightly. Variable-speed drives can be used for the same purpose. *In either case, the intent should be to limit the frequency of pumps turning on and off.* The operator at one 20-MGD facility told the author that turning on all his pumps at the same time would result in a $10,000 peak demand charge from the electric company. The electrical demand charges are an important factor in the operation of pumps. If the system allows, there may be off-peak demand periods with lower electrical charges, during which pumping can take place. In terms of operational costs, sizing the pumps to operate properly and efficiently is one of the more important aspects of providing an economical design. To help designers, the US Department of Energy maintains sizing guidelines for pumping systems, which are readily accessible.

Throttling

As an alternative to multiple pumps, it may be possible to satisfy small changes in demand by throttling a pump. Throttling is accomplished by increasing or decreasing the pump discharge pressure

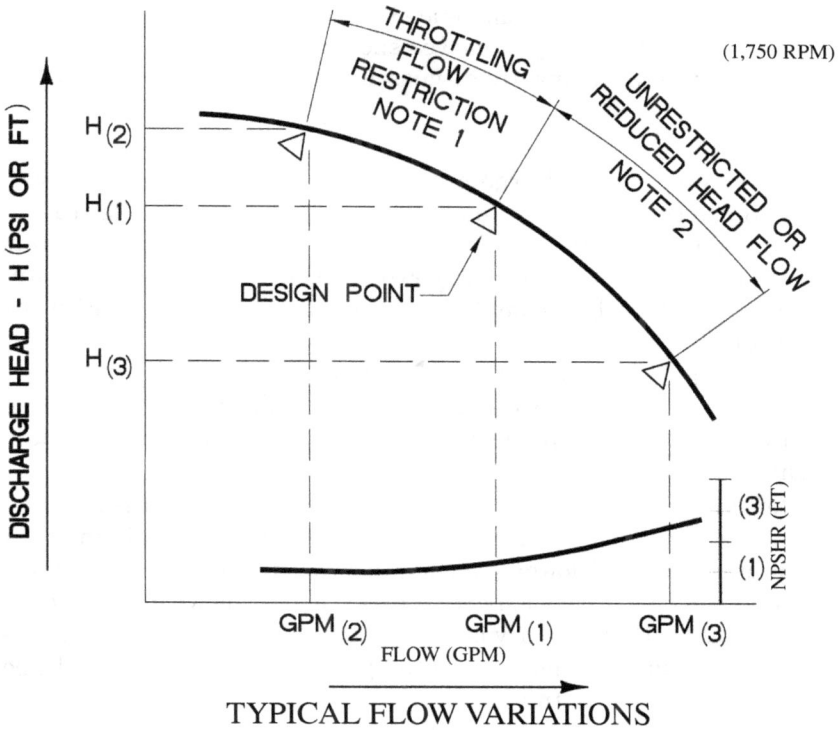

TYPICAL FLOW VARIATIONS

Notes:
1. Throttling reduces flow, increases pressure,
    and may reduce horsepower.
2. Reduced head and increased flow raises NPSH
    requirements and can cause cavitation.

Figure 3-1   Effects of throttling

by way of a modulating valve on the pump discharge. The effects of throttling a pump by increasing or decreasing the discharge pressure are illustrated on Figure 3-1.

The suction side of a pump should never be throttled, because it increases the net positive suction head required (NPSHR) and can cause the pump to lose prime and cavitate.

Closing a valve on the pump discharge can increase pressure and decrease flow up to the shutoff or no-flow condition. On the other hand, changing the operating point by opening a discharge valve may be limited by the normal backpressure of the system.

In either case, it is recommended that the operating point *not* be moved outside the family of curves shown in Figure 2-4. Several issues related to throttling are discussed in the following sections.

Increasing Pressure

Increasing the discharge pressure of a pump moves its operating point to the left on the impeller curve, as shown in Figure 3-1. The pressure may increase slightly because of changing system demands such as a higher reservoir level. However, significant changes are usually accomplished by partly closing a valve on the pump discharge.

Increasing the head loss by an amount of $H_2 - H_1$ on Figure 3-1 moves the operating point to the left, and the flow is reduced from GPM_1 to GPM_2. At the same time, the NPSHR is also reduced slightly.

Referring to the typical curves in Chapter 2 (Figures 2-4 to 2-9), moving to the left on the impeller curve may also result in lower pump efficiency and lower horsepower requirements. Some vertical line shaft turbine pumps may be an exception, along with other types. In Figure 2-13, the efficiency is reduced toward the left, but the horsepower requirements remain essentially constant for the vertical line shaft turbine pump in this case.

In sizing a pump for different flow conditions (or pressure), it is important that it meet the design flow at the minimum system pressure, as well as the maximum. In addition, if a pump is to be throttled back, an allowance for pressure modulation, above the minimum, should be included in the design calculations.

Effects of Reduced Pressure

Figure 3-2 illustrates the effect of reducing the pump pressure, causing it to operate farther to the right on its impeller curve. Changing the discharge conditions will move the operating point either to the left or to the right, but it will always be on the impeller curve. If the discharge pressure is reduced, the pump will operate farther to the right, and the impeller curve may cross over a horsepower curve, as shown in Figure 3-2. If the pump is allowed to operate to the right, as shown in this figure, then it should be provided with a motor large enough so that it is *nonoverloading across the range.*

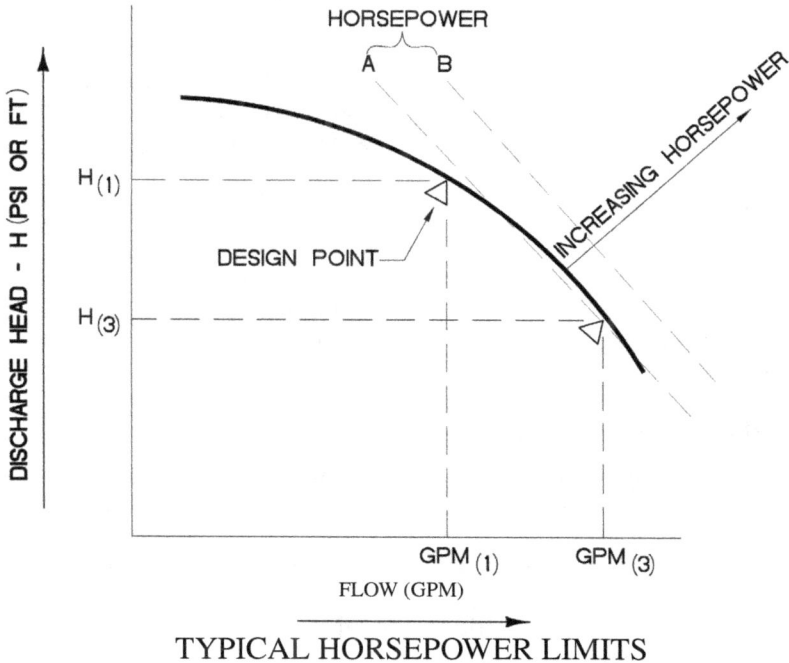

TYPICAL HORSEPOWER LIMITS

Notes:
1. Increased flow due to reduced head can also exceed
    the available horsepower and burn up the motor.
2. Choose a motor size that is nonoverloading over the
    entire range of the pump.

Figure 3-2   Effects of throttling on motor size

Increased NPSHR

In addition to increasing horsepower, operating to the right of the design point will also increase the net positive suction head requirement.

Assuming that the pump operates properly at the design point, it
may not run properly if allowed to run too far to the right. For that
reason, the motor could overheat and cavitate. Therefore, the allowable operating conditions should be well defined so as not to exceed
the capability of the pump.

Seasonal Variations

Assuming a raw water intake, the pump might be able to operate
to the right of its design point in the winter, when the river or suction-

side water level is high. However, when that water level goes down, it will reduce the net positive suction head available, and the pump may not be able to operate very far to the right of the design point. If the suction-side water level does vary, a flow control device may be needed to keep the pump operating within its capability.

Variable-Speed-Drive Systems

As an option to throttling, variable-speed-drive systems are often used to modulate the flow of a pump. There are magnetic drive systems, variable-frequency drives, and others. However, for the purposes of this discussion, variable-frequency drives will be used as the model.

Variable-Frequency Drives (VFDs)

A simplified diagram of a VFD is shown in Figure 3-3. A standard three-phase power supply is brought into the VFD cabinet. A rectifier then modifies it to direct-current power (DC). A percentage dial or control then regulates or modifies the direct current, which is then sent to a converter to change it back to a slightly different frequency three-phase power. It should be noted that VFDs are used in this manner to reduce the speed of a motor.

Variable-Speed Pump Calculations

As stated previously, a pump will operate on its impeller curve. If the motor speed is reduced, the operating point is moved downward and to the left, as shown in Figure 3-4. At this reduced speed, a new impeller curve is generated parallel to the original. In Figure 3-4, the

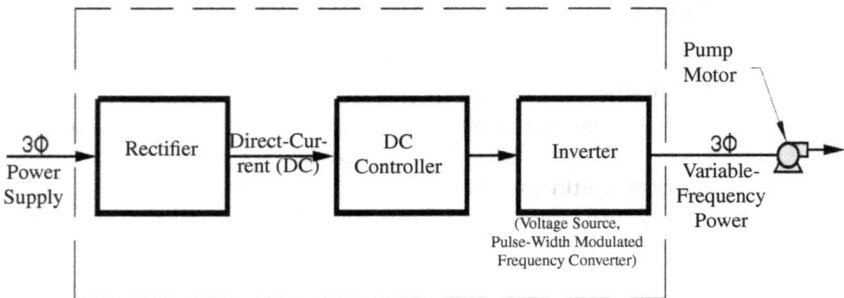

Note: The VFD varies the speed and torque of the motor.

Figure 3-3   Variable-frequency drive

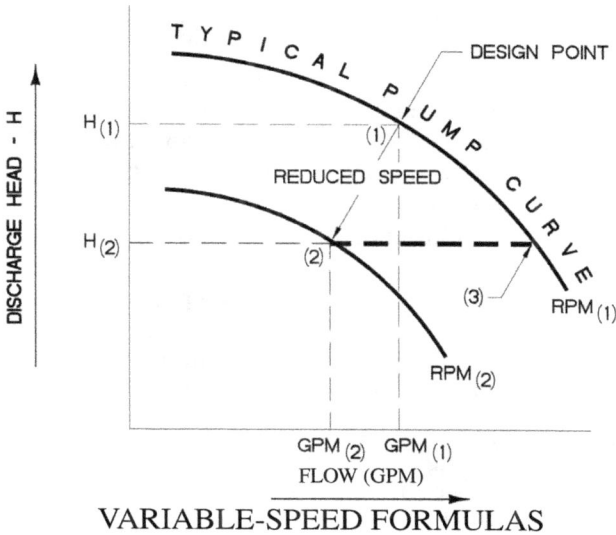

VARIABLE-SPEED FORMULAS

$$\frac{GPM_2}{GPM_1} = \frac{RPM_2}{RPM_1} \qquad \frac{H_2}{H_1} = \left(\frac{RPM_2}{RPM_1}\right)^2 \qquad \frac{HP_2}{HP_1} = \left(\frac{RPM_2}{RPM_1}\right)^3$$

Notes:
1. $H_{(2)}$ cannot be lower than the static head of the system.
2. Providing the ability to reduce speed in a high static head system may result in a larger pump and motor.

Figure 3-4   Variable-speed pump calculations

original operating point is shown as H_1 (pressure) and GPM_1 (flow). When the speed is reduced, a new pressure, H_2, and flow, GPM_2, are produced. The results of changing pump and motor speed are defined by a set of formulas as shown on the bottom of Figure 3-4. The flow varies directly with the pump speed such that a reduction of 10 percent in speed also results in a reduction of 10 percent of flow.

The change in pressure from H_1 to H_2 varies according to the square of the ratio of speed. For example, if the flow is reduced by 10 percent, the pressure is reduced by 19 percent. The horsepower varies according to the cube of the change in speed. If the flow is reduced by 10 percent, the horsepower is reduced by 27 percent.

VFD Design

For design purposes, assume that a pump is operating in a typical system, as shown in Figure 1-1, wherein the pump is lifting water to a receiving reservoir at a defined static head. In that case, there will be a maximum and a minimum water level condition. When designing a VFD in this set of circumstances, the pump should be designed at the reduced speed condition that satisfies the minimum system pressure requirement. In other words, regardless of percent speed, the pump must still produce enough pressure to lift the water the minimum distance at the lowest operating condition.

If the flow is to be reduced by 10 percent, 90 percent of capacity will be pumped at the lower static head. On the other hand, to increase the flow from 90 percent to 100 percent, the pressure is increased by 19 percent, and the horsepower required is 27 percent greater than at the lower static head. In other words, changing the speed has a dramatic impact on the design of a pump and the system.

Actual Pump Curves

To illustrate the effect of varying the pump speed, two sets of actual curves are provided for the same pump at different motor speeds. Figure 3-5 illustrates a pump operating at 1,750 rpm. The operating point is shown at Q_1 = 1,700 gpm, the pressure H_1 is 218 ft, and the horsepower required, HP_1, is 125 horsepower. The second curve is shown in Figure 3-6, wherein the motor speed is 1,150 rpm. The flow Q_2 is 1,125 gpm. The pressure H_2 is 95 ft, and the horsepower required, HP_2, is 30 horsepower.

Low Speed Operating Point

The flow at 1,150 rpm is approximately two thirds of that at 1,750 rpm. The change in operating conditions in this case is substantial. The horsepower required was reduced from 125 to 30, and the pressure from 218 ft to 95 ft of water. While the reduction in horsepower looks good, it is important to remember that the designer has to consider things from the bottom up. To operate at the reduced flow, the pump pressure is 95 ft. If the actual static head is greater than that, the pump cannot operate at the reduced speed of 1,150 rpm. In addition, only a 30-horsepower motor is needed at the lower speed. To increase the speed to 1,750 rpm requires an additional 95 horsepower. In other words, to reduce the speed according to this example will result in having a 125-horsepower motor that is only producing 30 horsepower at low speed. When the speed is increased to the full 1,750 rpm, the pump pressure increases from 90 ft to 218 ft.

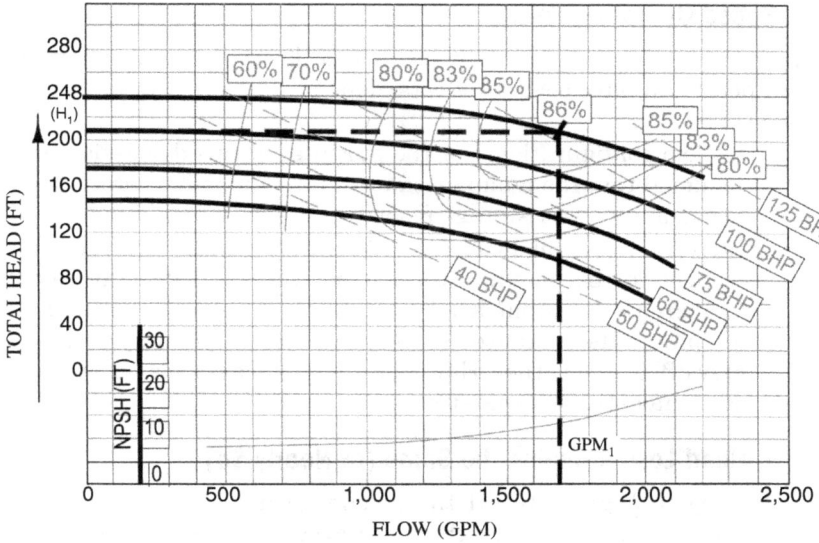

Note: Scale = 100 gpm per square.

Figure 3-5   1,750-rpm pump curve

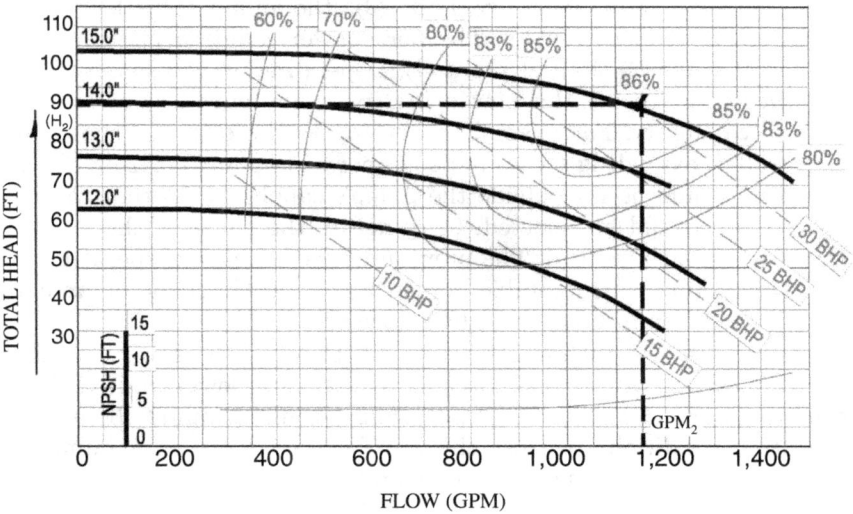

Note: Scale = 100 gpm per square.

Figure 3-6   1,150-rpm pump curve

High-Speed Operating Point

Increasing the flow from the low-speed design to the high-speed design point can have several effects, depending on the configuration of the system.

- System configuration. For the purposes of this discussion, it is assumed that the pump discharges into a pipeline, which leads to a gravity water storage reservoir as shown in Figure 1-1.
- Increased system head loss. When the pump is large with respect to the pipeline, increasing the flow rate may result in increased system head loss. Depending on the design of the pump, the increased system head loss and pump pressure may offset each other. However, in many cases the pump pressure may still be excessive.

System Head Loss Remains the Same (or Nearly So)

Referring to Figure 3-4, if the discharge head H1 at the high-speed design point is greater than the system pressure, the pump operating point will move to the right on the curve. For example if the system pressure is still H_2, the operating point will move to point (3), assuming no substantial change in pipe friction.

When increasing speed to move from point (2) to point (1), the variable-speed formulas on Figure 3-4 are always in effect. However, when moving from there to point (3), the pump impeller curve requirements are in control. The horsepower required may then be higher at point (3) than at point (1). Depending on the shape of the specific pump curve, the new operating point may be outside the pump's capability. For example, referring to the example shown in Figure 3-7, extending the low-speed operating point horizontally to the right would be far outside the pump's capability. In that case, a new pump should be selected. Once again, the shape of the pump's impeller curve is critical. The pump must be capable of operating at all three points, with suitable horsepower for each. If the pump can satisfy these conditions, it will be a good choice.

Assuming the theoretical curve on Figure 3-4, extending the operating point would work, as long as the horsepower and NPSHR conditions are met. The O&M personnel should compare the actual operating conditions against the impeller curve for each pump to verify that the pump is capable of operating as required.

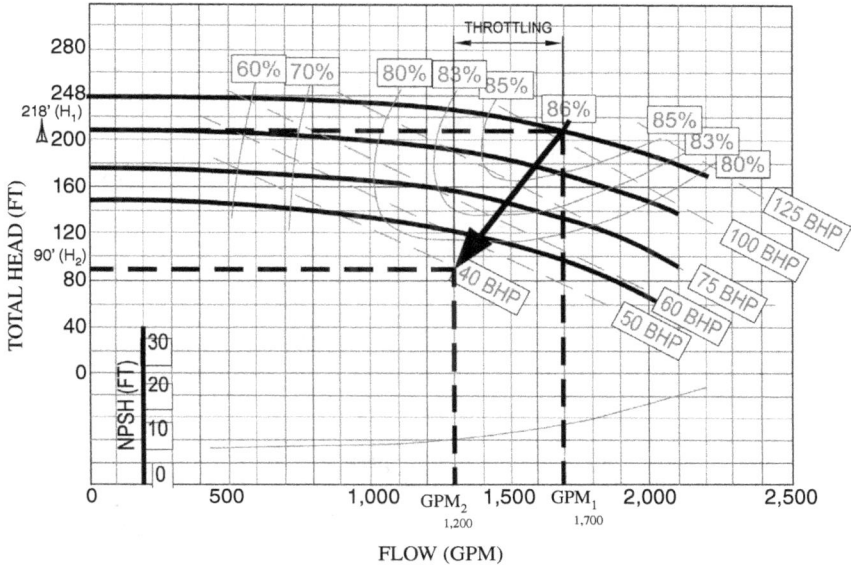

Note: Scale = 100 gpm per square.

Figure 3-7 Comparison of 1,750- versus 1,150-rpm speed

Comparison of Operating Conditions

A comparison of the two operating conditions is shown in Figure 3-7. It should be noted that varying the speed this much is an extreme example and is not recommended. For one thing, the horsepower requirements vary too much.

In the case previously described, throttling from the high flow (GPM_1) to the low flow (GPM_2) only results in a reduction of 25 horsepower. In this case, throttling might be more economical than providing a variable-speed drive. It is recommended that an economic evaluation be made to determine the most efficient method of varying the flow.

Benefits of a VFD System

Variable-frequency-drive (VFD) pump systems are often used to match small variations in demand. Many large water treatment plants discharge to a receiving reservoir that only holds a portion of a day's capacity. In that case, it may be necessary to match production with demand fairly closely, to prevent the receiving reservoir from running dry. (See Figure 3-8.)

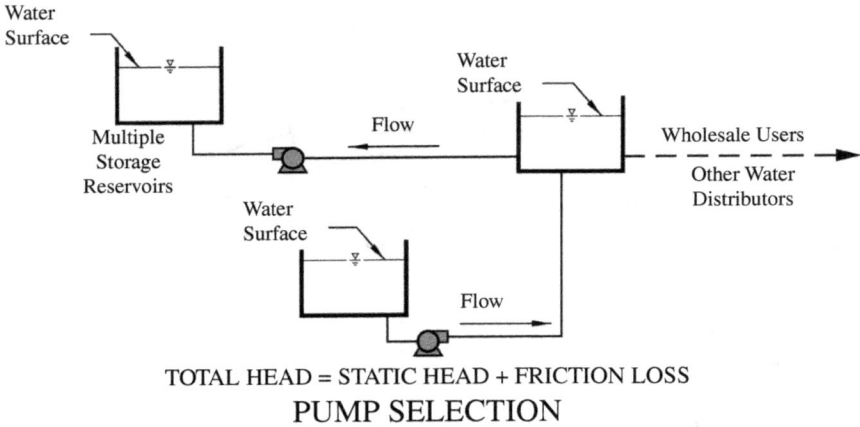

TOTAL HEAD = STATIC HEAD + FRICTION LOSS
PUMP SELECTION

Figure 3-8   Large potable water system operation

A major benefit of a VFD system is to keep large pumps from repeatedly starting and stopping. If multiple pumps are being used, one *trim pump* with a VFD may be used to match the desired flow without starting or stopping any of the others. In this way, only one pump needs to have a VFD, even when there are multiple pumps in a water system.

VFD Design Considerations

In providing a VFD in a new installation, all the components can be designed accordingly. However, in a retrofit, installing a VFD is not as simple as changing the motor starter. All the components need to be carefully addressed. The system design needs to be analyzed, as discussed previously, and an electrical engineer should be consulted for the actual installation. Several issues are noted in the following list:

1. A VFD normally requires a larger motor and heavier wiring from the motor starter. Special motors may be used that are provided with reinforced insulation.

2. A VFD is only about 96 or 97 percent efficient. The difference in efficiency results in the generation of substantial heat in the motor starter, which must be dissipated. As a result, the electrical room containing the VFD may require additional ventilation or air conditioning. The author has witnessed more than one installation with inadequate ventilation that had a house fan cooling an open VFD cabinet.

3. VFDs are not recommended for high static head applications. Because of the relationships between speed and horsepower, a much larger motor is typically needed for high static head applications and may not be the most efficient installation.

4. Other design issues to be addressed by the electrical engineer include larger wiring required, potential resonance with other equipment, long cable runs, and potential induced voltages.

Pump Efficiency Factors

As mentioned previously, it is important to select a pump that is operating at or near its peak efficiency range. The designer should be aware that impeller design and efficiency have changed in the last 20 years, so that newer designs are 5 to 10 percent more efficient. If the pump is that old, consideration should be given to replacing it.

Motor Efficiency

There has also been a 5 to 10 percent increase in motor efficiency over the last 20 years. Motors with an efficiency of 94 percent or greater are available, while submersible motors are in the range of 85 percent efficient.

Replacement Evaluation

The designer and operations personnel should be aware that simply installing a VFD on an existing pump may not work, unless the pump has excess capacity. The VFD will make the pump operate at lower flows and pressure than before. An economic evaluation may be necessary to determine if a motor should be replaced, or if the entire pump and motor assembly should be replaced. Initial capital costs, maintenance costs, and electrical power costs should be considered in a complete life-cycle analysis.

Pump Capacity Options

When sizing the pump in terms of percent demand, there are a number of variables to consider, including system size, present versus future demand, variations in the existing demand, and economics. There are many designs for pump systems. Some pumps operate off of line pressure to boost the water to a different level. Others operate in wet wells or river intakes. A minimum suction-side pressure of 20 psi is normally required for pumps operating off of line pressure.

With pumps operating in river intakes or wet wells/sumps, the designer also must take into account the physical sizing and configuration of the wet well or sump.

System Size

In a small system, there may be only one pump to satisfy 100 percent demand. The overall system may be small, or a small pump may feed a small upper-level pressure zone off a larger system. The liability in having only one pump is that the system will be totally off line if that pump fails.

Present Versus Future Demand

A water master plan for a system should include predictions of the future demand as well as a review of present operation. Only one pump may be needed presently, whereas a second or third pump may be required in the future to meet the anticipated increase in demand. Even if only one pump is provided, space, valves, and connections may be provided to allow easy installation of a future set of pumps. All this information should be made available to O&M personnel.

Variations in System Demand

The demand of many water systems typically varies during any given day and also seasonally. Holidays may also generate a change in system demand. Variations in system demand are often taken into account by using a storage reservoir that feeds water back to the users. In that case, a pump can run all day at an average flow, allowing the reservoir to be depleted during the day and refilled at night. There are occasions, with reservoirs also, where the pumps are required to provide a variable flow. Small receiving reservoirs or constant-pressure pumping systems are an example.

In a constant-pressure pumping application, the author has often provided one small pump to operate all the time to maintain system pressure. When the demand increases, the pressure will begin to drop, and a second or third pump can then come on to satisfy the demand. It is desirable even in small systems to prevent the pumps from turning on and off frequently. In addition to higher electrical demand, it causes wear and tear on the motor and motor starters. The term *jockey pump* is used by the author to describe the small pump in this system. Other names may be used, but the intent is the same.

Water System Optimization

A capital improvements plan (CIP) is recommended as the first step in ensuring the highest-efficiency operation of a water system. A CIP may call for increasing the size of small piping to lower the pumping pressure required. A CIP may include the replacement of motors and old, inefficient pumps, and larger wet wells. It may specify control modifications to reduce pump starts and stops, the use of multiple pump sizes, or VFD trim pumps.

Summary

The most efficient pump is usually a fixed-speed unit operating at its maximum available efficiency. However, the system may need a variable-speed trim pump to provide proper service. Whatever the individual needs, a complete systems approach, including an economic evaluation, is recommended prior to modifying or adding to a system. If the addition of a pump with a variable-speed drive can keep other pumps from cycling on and off frequently, the VFD will be a highly economical choice. All planning and design information should be made available to the O&M personnel and contained in a manual to be maintained on site with other information recommended in this handbook.

CHAPTER 4

Pump Troubleshooting

Introduction

The purpose of pumps is to lift a fluid to a higher elevation. They are an essential component of most utility systems, including potable water, industrial/commercial applications, and sewage collection and treatment. Pumps usually perform a function as part of a system and must be designed to operate within the requirements of that system. Troubleshooting a pump often involves an analysis of the system as well.

Although there are many pump types, this discussion will be limited to typical operational and design problems on some of the more common types, such as centrifugal, line shaft turbine, and solids-handling pumps. If the discharge pressure and flow rate of an operating pump are close to the design point, the pump is fulfilling its function. On the other hand, if the pump is not producing as designed, or if it is vibrating or exhibiting any other problems, an investigation should be made to resolve and repair any deficiencies.

The following are some of the troubleshooting procedures used and recommended by the author.

Close Coupled Centrifugal Pumps

Preliminary Evaluation

For a close coupled centrifugal pump (Figure 4-1), the first and simplest evaluation to be performed is to determine if the pump is performing as designed and if it is vibrating excessively.

Vibration. The vibration should be minimal, and the motor should feel like it's running "smooth" or very even. In addition, the motor temperature should be normal. If the pump is vibrating, there are several potential causes, such as worn bearings or seals, or cavitation. Bearings and seals should be replaced per the manufacturer's recommendations. If the problems reoccur, the piping and other devices on the suction side should be evaluated for cavitation or other inlet problems.

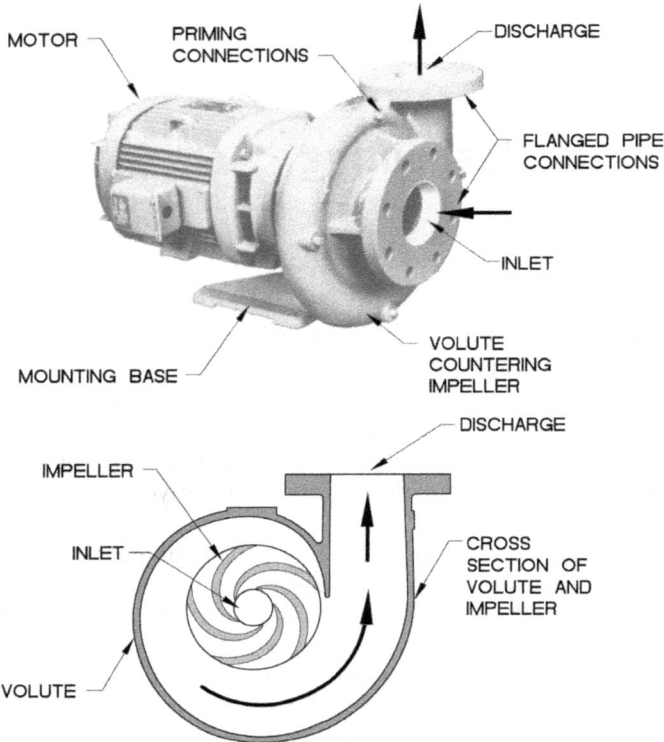

Figure 4-1   Typical close coupled centrifugal pump

Refer also to the discussion on sump design for pumps using them. A very warm or hot motor may indicate similar problems as previously mentioned. The allowable temperature rise (above ambient) is usually listed on the motor nameplate. If the temperature appears to be higher than it should be, the motor and/or pump may be in danger of failure and should be replaced or repaired as soon as possible.

Performance. The second test is to determine if the pump is producing the design pressure and flow. The pump should be in reasonable condition if it is running smoothly and performing properly. However, it is still necessary to do the recommended maintenance.

Flowmeter

If a flowmeter indicates loss of capacity in a pump, the entire installation should be inspected for proper operation. If all else appears normal, the meter should be calibrated. Old flowmeters and those with rotating or moving parts are especially suspect, and may need maintenance or replacement themselves.

Pressure Boost

In the absence of a meter, the flow can be approximated if the upstream and downstream pressures around the pump are known. Using the difference in pressures (pressure boost), refer to the actual pump impeller curve, if available, as demonstrated in Figure 2-10. The flow can be approximated using the pressure reading. Determining the flow and pressure in this way is one of the simplest and easiest ways to evaluate the operating condition of a pump.

When there is a suction lift, a vacuum gauge must be used on the suction side of the pump or an actual measurement taken. The vacuum reading can be compared against the norm, from normal conditions and/ or the value from the recommended maintenance/design manual, and added to the discharge pressure to calculate the total pressure boost.

For a vertical line shaft pump, the distance down to the sump or well water level must be added to the discharge pressure to calculate the total pressure boost.

Design Conditions

If the discharge pressure and flow rate are close to the design point, the pump is fulfilling its function. It may still have mechanical problems, such as vibration, suction-side restrictions, or hydraulic sump design, which need to be identified and addressed before production is affected.

Low Flow/Pressure

A lower than normal flow or discharge pressure obviously indicates that there are most likely problems that need to be identified and repaired. Lower than normal design flow could be the result of a number of factors, including the following:

Cavitation. Cavitation can be caused by unstable operation, which vaporizes some of the water, creating bubbles that pass through the pump. Pressure created by the pump can cause these bubbles to collapse, creating a knocking or tapping sound on the discharge pipe. Formation and collapse of the air bubbles can, in turn, cause pitting and excessive wear on the inlet side of the pump and impeller. Causes of cavitation include too high of a flow rate, which means the pump is operating too far to the right on its curve, or restrictions in the inlet piping, causing the pump to exceed its NPSH requirements, which can also result in overheating and pump failure.

Restriction in inlet piping. Fouling or restriction of the inlet piping can raise the NPSH to a value that may be higher than that available. Leaks in the suction piping, especially in a suction lift condition, can also cause similar problems, including loss of prime and overheating of the pump and motor. If a suction problem is suspected, it may be necessary to disassemble some of the suction-side piping for inspection. The author once found a pipe gasket in the pump influent piping. A small beaver got caught in the inlet piping at another facility.

Small inlet piping. In general, the suction connection on a pump is larger than the discharge connection. The smaller discharge piping is used because of higher velocity. The purpose of larger suction piping is to reduce head loss, minimize NPSH, and provide a low, uniform approach velocity to the pump. The calculations shown previously in Figures 2-1 and 2-2 can be used to determine if there is too much suction-side head loss.

High flow rate. The net positive suction head required (NPSHR) rises dramatically if a pump operates at too high of a flow rate, which is to the right on the family of curves. (See Figures 2-4 and 2-8.) There are situations where a pump could operate at a much higher flow than designed. For example, in a suction lift situation, if the source water level is higher than normal, there will be more positive suction pressure, and a higher flow is possible. However, in the same situation, a lowering of the source water level could result in loss of prime and overheating of the motor at the same flow rate. For reliable operation, the pump in this example should be limited to the normal design flow, even if it could operate faster part of the time.

To resolve the above situation, as a temporary measure, throttle the pump back to a higher pressure and a lower flow, where it can operate within its limits. Afterwards, the design conditions should be verified to determine where the pump can operate properly. In such a situation, it is recommended that the pump discharge be regulated automatically by a flowmeter and flow control valve. Such protection is especially recommended with large pumps and critical applications.

Application problems. During design, the pump selected should match the water quality and the system demands. For example, centrifugal pumps may not be the best application for dirty, high-solids water, especially if packing is used on a frame-mounted pump, which will be discussed in the next section. For dirty, high-solids water, a solids-handling pump may be the best choice.

If a pump is having frequent maintenance problems, the system should be evaluated to determine if the design conditions are correct or have changed, or if the proper pump is being used. For example, if large fluctuations in demand or system pressure are occurring, it may be necessary to change the pump, install multiple pumps, or use a variable-frequency drive (VFD) to compensate. It may also be necessary to install a stilling well, strainers, or other appropriate devices to remove the solids from the water, if the installation can be done without impacting the operation of the pump.

Piping connections. Piping full of water has a considerable weight. As such, heavy piping should be supported independently from the pump. Unsupported piping can break the pump casting. It can also create stress on bearings and result in failure as well as inhibit pump removal and repair. Therefore, it is recommended that piping be supported separately, close to the pump on all connections. Small threaded pipe connections might be an exception. However, support is always recommended.

Air release valves. Although not as common in flooded suction situations, air release valves can be found in treatment plants, long transmission mains, and other applications. Combination air/vacuum valves are often used to allow air to pass in either direction. However, in some applications the presence of air is undesirable.

Release-only valves can also be the *source* of air in low pressure situations (elevated piping is a possible example) and pipelines with very high velocity water that creates low static pressure.

It is recommended that the discharge of all air release-only valves be tested for air entering the valve. Most air release valves do not work well at low pressure. If air is entering, it is recommended that a rubber-seated check valve be installed on the release valve discharge to eliminate that possibility. Accessories may also be available to enable air release valves to operate properly at low pressure. It should be noted that specialty air release valves are available for use just downstream of vertical line shaft turbine pumps. The manufacturer should be consulted for recommendations for a specific application.

Frame-Mounted Centrifugal Pumps

Larger centrifugal pumps are often provided with an extended shaft, which must be mounted separately to a motor shaft with a coupling. The pump is mounted on a frame to keep the pump and motor shafts aligned properly.

Steel or cast-iron frames, and in special situations stainless steel, can be used to mount these pumps. A cast-iron frame is shown in Figure 4-2. In either case, the frame should be mounted to a concrete floor

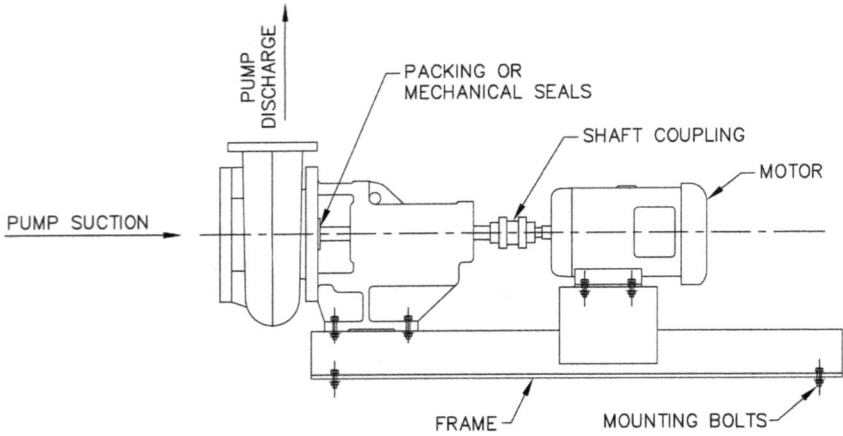

Figure 4-2   Frame-mounted centrifugal pump

or slab for proper anchorage. If steel frames are used, the frame could be filled with concrete for additional stability after installation.

For these pumps, a certified pump technician should check the shaft alignment after installation to ensure proper operation. If there is any vibration during start-up, the pump should be shut down until it can be inspected and repaired.

The comments on centrifugal pumps in the previous section will apply to frame-mounted types also. The following additional comments are provided for frame-mounted pumps.

Seals

Either packing or mechanical seals can be used on frame-mounted pumps. The choice depends on the service to some degree. It is recommended that the manufacturer be consulted for recommendations.

Packing. Packing consists of a ropelike material wound around the shaft and held in place by compression. If the packing is tightened too much, it can cause excessive shaft wear and subsequent vibration. Excessive grit can also cause shaft wear and the packing to leak. Packing often leaks, even when new. Therefore, it should be tightened only to the manufacturer's specifications, not necessarily until it stops leaking.

Mechanical. Theoretically, mechanical seals should not leak. However, grit can eventually cause them to leak, which may in turn create excessive wear and vibration. Therefore, if mechanical seals are provided, a fresh water flush is recommended for the pump to help keep the seal clean and free of grit.

In either case, whether using packing or mechanical seals, a frame-mounted pump should be provided with a drip shield and tubing to the nearest floor drain to keep the area clean and dry.

Vibration (Pump or Motor)

Shaft wear can be caused by cavitation, packing, or seal wear. A worn or misaligned shaft coupling or unsupported piping can also cause vibration. The section on close coupled pumps discusses additional recommendations regarding vibration.

Vertical In-Line Centrifugal Pumps

Vertical in-line centrifugal pumps (Figure 4-3) take up less floor space than other types and are often used for that reason. These pumps operate in the same manner as and have similar problems and solutions as other types of centrifugal pumps discussed previously. However, a vertical in-line pump has an extra set of thrust bearings/bushings because of the vertical orientation, which also require periodic replacement.

Vertical Line Shaft Turbine Pumps

Vertical line shaft turbine pumps (Figure 4-4) are commonly used in process applications for intakes and final effluent distribution pumps. They are not preferred by the author for applications with high solids. Typical problems include those below.

Inadequate Submergence

For each size and type of pump, there is a minimum amount of water depth, or submergence, required over the suction inlet bell. Lower water levels can cause a vortex to be created on the surface of the water, which allows air to be drawn into the pump. The result can be vibration and unstable operation. The minimum submergence required will, therefore, dictate the lowest water level at which the sump or clearwell can be operated. If submergence is an issue, the designer may have to allow for a trench along one end of the clearwell or sump to allow the pump to be installed lower for adequate operational depth.

In an existing system, if the submergence is a problem, controls would have to be adjusted to prevent the water level from being drawn

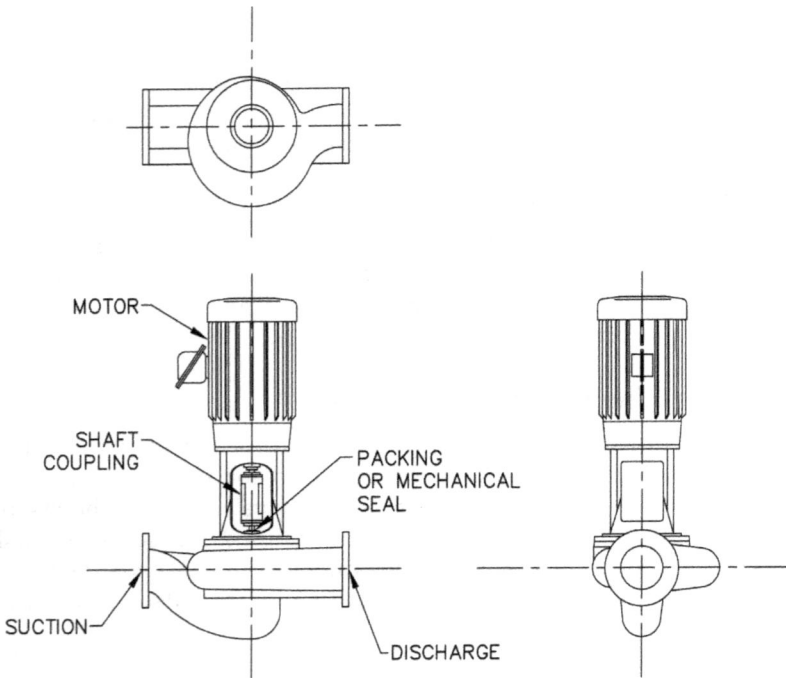

Figure 4-3   Vertical centrifugal pump

down below the minimum submergence level. The manufacturer
should be contacted for the requirements for each specific pump.

Application Issues

A vertical line shaft turbine pump may have multiple impellers at
the bottom of a pipe column. The column consists of various sections
of pipe suspended from the discharge head assembly above. The pump
drive shaft goes down through the middle of the pipe column to the
impellers below. The water drawn in by the impellers is then pushed
up through the pipe column to the discharge head assembly, where the
water turns 90 degrees and is discharged horizontally. At each pipe
connection on the pipe column, there is also a shaft connection consisting of a coupling and rubber bushings to keep the shaft centered.

Grit/dirty water. Grit and dirt can cause wear to the bearings
and rubber bushings at each shaft coupling as the water passes. As a
result, a vertical line shaft turbine pump should not be used for situations where there is dirt, grit, or high solids content in the water.

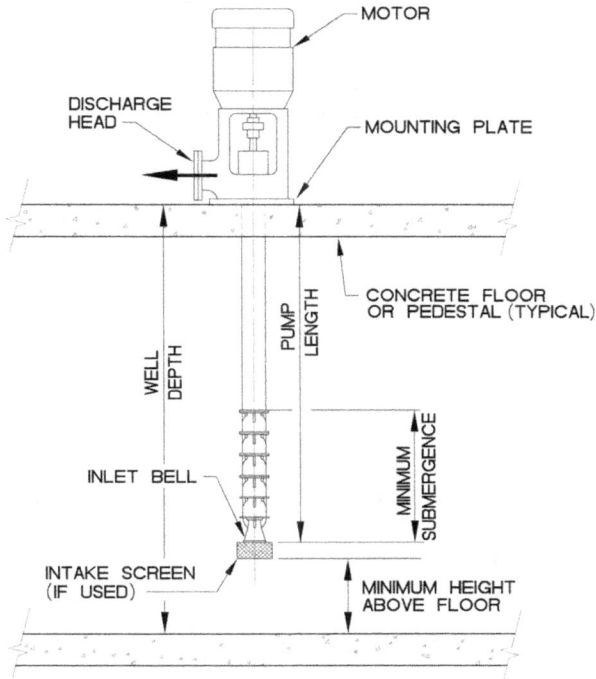

Figure 4-4   Typical vertical line shaft turbine pump

In such a situation, a fresh clean water supply is recommended for a bearing and seal flush. A flushing assembly will help the situation but will not entirely resolve the problem.

Vegetable oil used on one deep well pump for lubrication caused a large buildup of coagulated oil down in the well that resembled cottage cheese. Oil is not recommended for that reason.

Turbulence at the pump inlet. Turbulence at the pump inlet can cause unstable operation, where water comes in one side of the inlet bell and is thrown out the other. Such turbulence can cause shaft vibration and excessive wear to the bushings and impellers. (See Figures 3-8 and 2-14.) Operating in an unstable flow situation (Figure 2-13) can also cause shaft vibration and excessive wear.

Pipe Column

A problem unique to vertical line shaft turbine pumps is presented by the pipe column from the pump head down to the impellers. The pipe column is typically made of painted steel. Over time, the steel can rust, causing pinholes in the pipe and leaks. A leaking pipe column can allow air in, as a result of high water velocity. Leaks of this type typically cause milky-looking water at the pump discharge and can cause improper readings in instrumentation.

A leak of air inward, during operation, may be detected, just after the pump is shut off, by the presence of water leaking out. The wet well must be accessible for that purpose. At one facility, the O&M personnel repaired such a leak with a pipe repair band on a temporary basis until permanent repairs could be made.

Wet Well Design

There are many examples of proper wet well design. However, the important criterion is for the water to approach the pump in a straight, uniform manner, and as slowly as reasonably possible. Water should not be made to turn just before it reaches the pump, or it may cause turbulence or a prerotation of the water, which can cause unstable operation. (See Figure 3-8.) Similar problems can occur if water has to go past one pump to approach another. All the pumps should have a straight, even, uniform flow coming toward each of them separately for proper operation. If necessary, straightening vanes in the wet well can be used to smooth out the approach.

Submersible Pumps

There are two different kinds of pumps that come under the category of submersible: well pumps and solids-handling pumps.

Well Pumps

In a well pump assembly, the motor is on the bottom, with the impellers above, all of which is suspended by a pipe column, which also carries the water upward. (See Figure 2-16.)

Centering "spiders" (a special type of bushing) are needed between the pipe column and the well casing. With this type of assembly, the torque from the motor is adequate to swing the pipe column. If the pump is allowed to swing far enough to contact the well casing, the motor could overheat and fail. The motor relies on water passing by it to keep it cool. The author has inspected pumps where such a condition occurred. A burned spot on the motor casing was easily visible where it came in contact with the well casing and overheated. To keep the pump cool, the pump is often set at an appropriate depth so that most of the water will be drawn up past the motor to the impellers from below.

When well pumps are running, it is common for the water level in the well to be drawn down a certain amount. The amount of drawdown depends on the capacity of the aquifer, the size of the well casing, and the capacity of the well pump. The maximum drawdown expected must be added to the desired discharge pressure of the pump in order to size it properly. The pump must also be installed well below that point.

Power cables for the motor are generally strapped to the pump casing from the ground surface down to the motor. In addition, several monitoring functions may be wired back to the control panel to indicate the possibility of an alarm condition, such as moisture in the motor or overheating. A level probe is also common. These alarms are highly recommended to protect the pump and to help prevent a total failure.

Submersible Solids-Handling Pumps

These pumps are designed to handle solids up to 2 in. to 3 in. in diameter or more. Solids-handling pumps are not common in water systems. However, they can be used for removing accumulated solids from an intake or in solids-handling systems. Whatever the application, they are typically installed in a wet well or sump, which must be sized appropriately. On the other hand, too large a sump could cause wastewater to turn septic. The pump and wet well combination should be designed so that the pump does not come on and off rapidly. Frequent starting and stopping of the pump could cause excessive power use and wear to the motor.

As with a vertical line shaft turbine pump, there is a minimum submergence that must be maintained in the wet well. If the water is allowed to go below that point, the pump could create a vortex and air could enter the pump, causing unstable operation.

Because a submersible pump is inaccessible while it is operating, there are only limited means of detecting potential problems.

Power draw. Determining the power draw at the motor starter is relatively simple with the correct instruments. Too high a power draw could mean the pump suction is fouled. Even pumps with inlet cutting blades can become fouled. If fouling occurs often, some type of bar screen may be necessary on the incoming wastewater to protect the pump.

Moisture and overheating alarms. These alarms should not occur often to the same pump. If they do, there may be a manufacturing defect. When these alarms do occur, the pump needs to be removed from service and sent to a repair facility that specializes in submersible pumps and motor repair.

Frequent starting and stopping. If this is occurring, determine if the distance between the on/off levels can be widened. If it is not possible, it may be necessary to install smaller pumps.

Maintenance

There are two types of maintenance: scheduled (preventative) and crisis management.

Scheduled Maintenance

Maintenance recommended by the manufacturer can be scheduled in advance, hopefully before problems occur. Also, when maintenance is scheduled, the necessary parts can be obtained in advance and downtime can be minimized.

Crisis Management

Although a strong term, catastrophic failure can occur when maintenance is deferred. In such a case, poor performance may occur for a time prior to complete failure. When failure does occur, it may involve other system components as well, and usually entails a much greater expense than scheduled or recommended maintenance.

Conducting proper maintenance procedures in a timely manner may be difficult in small systems with inadequate staff. Budgeting for the expense is often difficult also. Small systems often have the same operational and maintenance problems, only with fewer staff and a smaller budget than larger systems.

Required maintenance is not something that can be delayed because the equipment appears to be working well. Whether intended or not, delayed maintenance results in crisis management. Besides being poor practice, it may result in higher costs for repair. Those in charge of water systems also have the responsibility of maintaining such equipment in the best interests of the public that is served. Pumps are often the most expensive component of a water system to operate, and they should be properly maintained.

Recommendations

On-Site Records

It is recommended that an O&M manual be prepared for each pump and that a copy be kept on site at all times. The following information is recommended:

1. Hydraulic profile of the system, including elevation of the pump and the level of the receiving reservoir.

2. Design conditions, including discharge pressure, pressure boost, suction-side conditions, and flow rate, with any anticipated variations in system demand.

3. Head loss design calculations.

4. Horsepower calculations.

5. The complete family of curves for each pump, with the operating point highlighted.

This information will greatly assist the operations staff in both understanding the workings of the system and determining when problems occur.

Maintenance Chart

A maintenance chart should be developed for each pump in each system and included in the on-site maintenance manual. The maintenance plan should include a schedule for regular lubrication, a schedule for frequent reading of pressure gauges and flowmeters, and any other tasks required on a routine basis.

Records

Any repairs should be listed on the maintenance sheet for the pump. If worn seals and bearings occur on a frequent basis, then an investigation of the complete installation and system requirements needs to be made to determine the cause of the pump problems so that the proper modifications can be made.

Use of the Maintenance Manual

It is not necessary for maintenance personnel to design or redesign a pump installation. However, the information recommended for inclusion in the maintenance manual will be very helpful to evaluate the system if problems occur. The information will also be helpful to determine the effect of any changed conditions.

The maintenance staff should ensure that the pressure gauges, flowmeters, and other accessories necessary to evaluate a pump are in place. The staff should recommend that all such equipment be provided if absent.

System-Wide Operation and Maintenance Plan or Implementing a *Green System*

In addition to the O&M tasks recommended for each pumping system, a system-wide plan should be developed by the owner including the following:

1.   Develop a hydraulic model of the system.
     •   Determine how each pump is supposed to function to allow the system to operate properly.
     •   Determine if there are any deficiencies, restrictions, or small piping that could be reconstructed to improve service and reduce costs. The author was once able to eliminate an entire pump station, resulting in a substantial savings to the owner in power costs.

2.   Evaluate each pump station and wet well.
     •   Pump size/age
     •   Wet well size (volume, area, and depth)
     •   Number of pump starts/stops per hour
     •   Motor and pump efficiencies
     •   Current vs. future flow

3.   Perhaps most importantly, develop a capital improvements plan (CIP) for upgrading and replacing pumps and piping systems and improving efficiency. The CIP should also include a schedule and budget allowance to make sure it is workable. O&M personnel should be included in the preparation of information for the CIP and should be allowed access to the final plan so they will know the expectations.

CHAPTER 5

Chemical Pumps

Introduction

There are numerous types of chemical feed pumps (Figure 5-1), and a wide variety of accessories available, depending on the application. Just as there are different pump types, there is a wide variety of chemicals used on water systems. For example, there are dilute chemicals such as liquid chlorine; corrosive chemicals such as potassium permanganate, ferric chloride, and fluosilicic acid; slurries such as carbon and lime; and viscous fluids such as polymers. Each of these has specific pumping requirements, including materials of construction, head design and construction, tubing size, flushing mechanisms, and other accessories.

The following discussion will focus primarily on diaphragm pumps, although several other types are also discussed.

Pump Types

Diaphragm Pumps

Basic operation. A diagram of a diaphragm pump is shown in Figure 5-2, along with an exploded view of the liquid end. Figure 5-3 illustrates a cutaway view of the same type of pump. An electromagnet in the pump activates a push-pull rod, which in turn pushes the diaphragm forward and pulls it back. The head, or liquid, end of the pump contains two ball check valves, one on the suction side and one on the discharge side, to facilitate operation of the pump when the diaphragm moves. A schematic of the liquid end of the diaphragm pump is shown in Figure 5-4, which includes the operating components of the pump.

Suction cycle. The suction cycle of the pump is illustrated in Figure 5-5. When the push-pull rod is pulled back, it pulls the diaphragm with it, creating suction in the head cavity, which in turn pulls the chemical up from below. A priming check valve on the bottom of the tubing keeps the suction tubing primed, while the suction check valve is pulled open during this part of the cycle. The head cavity is then filled with chemical from below. At the same time, the

Courtesy of Milton Roy America and Liquid Metronics (LMI)

Figure 5-1   New type of chemical feed pump

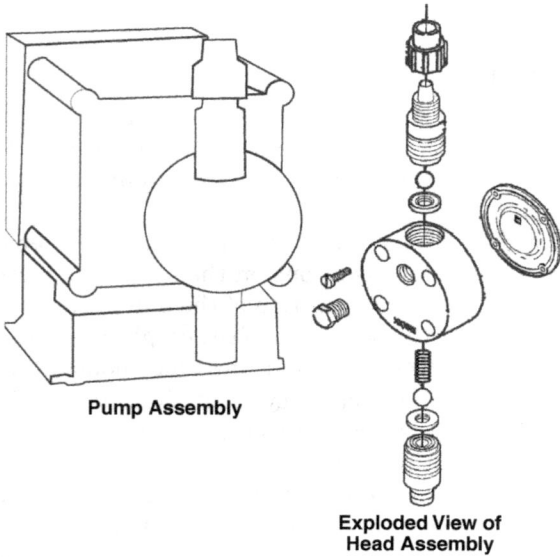

Pump Assembly

Exploded View of
Head Assembly

Figure 5-2   Diaphragm pumps

Durable Stroke Adjustment Mechanism

A rigid stroke bracket and large stroke knob offer precise, repeatable performance and simple adjustment over entire output range.

NEMA 4X/IP65 Housings

Totally enclosed, chemically resistant polypropylene housing for the ultimate protection against corrosive environments.

EPU

The Electromagnetic Power Unit (EPU) is designed for efficiency and consistent performance over a wide operating and temperature range.

Multi-Function Valves
The industry standard for over 25 years, features Fluorofilm™ diaphragms for long life and ramp style knobs for "hands free" priming with standard 3FV or optional 4FV. The auto prime valve option offers auto degassing for pumping chemicals prone to gassing.

Fluorofilm™ Liquiframs™
This unique manufacturing process of LMI diaphragms ensures outstanding chemical resistance and flexibility for long life.

Cartridge Valves
Unique cartridge valves have closely guided balls and triple sequential valve seats for optimum performance over entire pressure range.

Variety of Liquid Ends

A wide selection of liquid handling assemblies including PVDF, PVC, Acrylic, Polypropylene, 316 SS, and UHMWPE. Configurations for viscous chemicals and slurries provide flexibility in all applications.

Speed Control

Provides stroke rate and a turnaround ratio up to 100:1 for unmatched versitility.

Fully Encapsulated Electronics

Completely enclosed electronics provide protection against moisture, corrosive atmospheres and damage from vibration or mechanical shock.

Pump Status LED

Status LED provides a quick visual indication of pump speed and operation.

Manual or External Control

Dual-manual control of speed and stroke length or external control by means of a 4-20 mA or pulse imput for flow proportional applications and system integration.

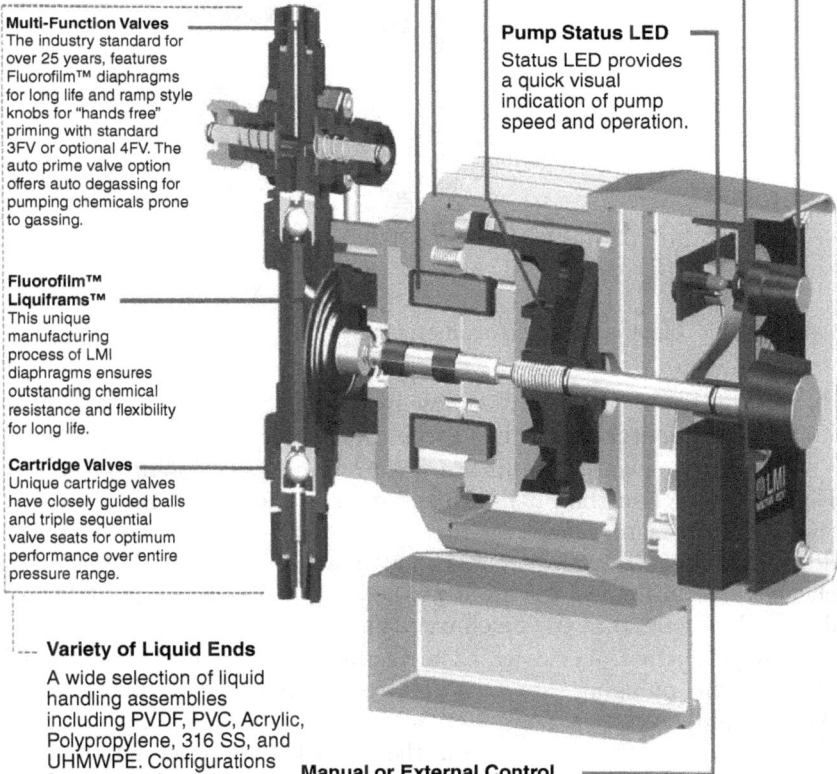

Courtesy of Milton Roy America and Liquid Metronics (LMI)

Figure 5-3   Diaphragm pump assembly

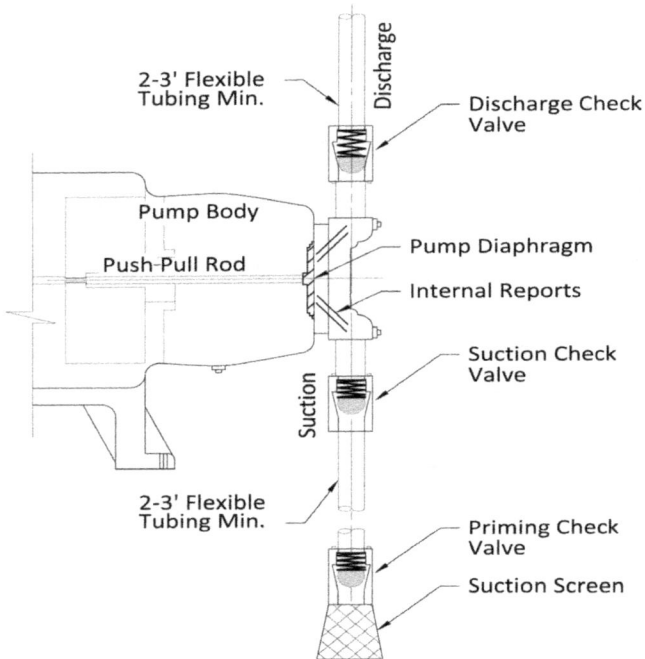

Figure 5-4   **Diaphragm pump head assembly**

discharge check valve is pulled downward and closed to prevent pump liquid from reentering the head from the system.

Discharge cycle. The discharge or pumping cycle is illustrated in Figure 5-6. When the push-pull rod pushes the diaphragm forward, the pressure is increased in the head cavity. The pressure pushes down and closes the suction check valve, while opening the discharge check valve, allowing the fluid pushed out of the head cavity to be directed upward into the discharge tubing.

Pump control. Typically, each diaphragm pump has two dials for adjusting the pumping rate. One dial (speed) regulates the frequency of the push-pull operation. *The faster the operation, the higher the pump discharge rate.* The second dial controls the stroke length. At a higher setting, the rod is pushed farther forward, flexing the diaphragm to its maximum limit in the head cavity. *The longer the stroke, the higher the capacity.*

Viscous solutions (polymers, etc.). When viscous solutions are to be pumped, the same basic pump components are used as discussed previously, with significant modifications. A pump for

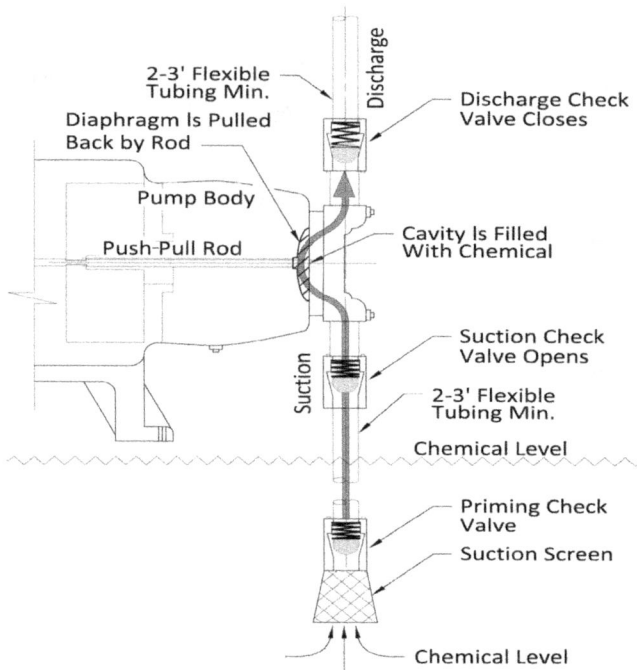

Figure 5-5   Diaphragm pump suction cycle

viscous solutions will use larger inlet and outlet tubing, as shown in Figure 5-7. In addition, the pump head has larger internal ports and a deeper diaphragm cavity to handle the high-viscosity fluid. High-viscosity fluids do not react well to high velocities or high pressure from rapid movement of the diaphragm. Therefore, the deeper cavity and larger porting is more suitable for viscous solutions.

Capacity. The author has observed polymer pumps that stalled and stopped pumping when the pump's capacity was used. Polymer pumps are often derated as much as 50 percent of their capacity to allow for the effects of viscosity.

Flooded suction. Many pumps, particularly smaller ones, may sit on top of the chemical feed tank and use a suction lift. However, with the heavier, thicker, more viscous polymers, a flooded suction is desired. It may be difficult to maintain a suction lift with any chemical if the pump is very far above the tank level. It is recommended that a lower connection or bulkhead fitting be provided on the bottom side of the tank to allow the pump to sit on or near the floor.

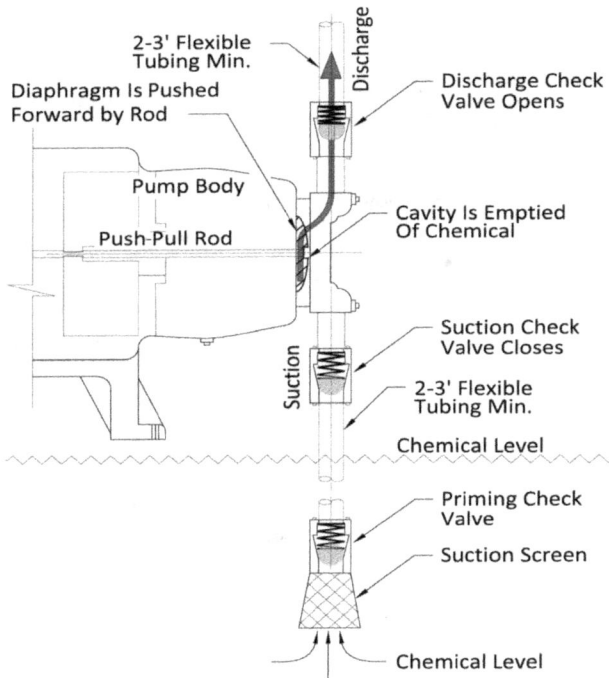

Figure 5-6   Diaphragm pump discharge cycle

Pumping distance. It is highly desirable to locate the chemical system relatively close to the point of injection to limit the distance that the pumped chemical must travel. Especially with viscous polymers, the discharge tubing/piping is prone to fouling over a period of time. In addition, the viscosity of the chemical will increase the friction head loss, which will increase the pumping pressure required.

Dilution/carrier water. For a more efficient system, it is common to provide a dilution/mixing system near the pump, such as is shown in Figure 5-8. In this system, the pumped chemical is mixed with a supply of clean dilution water, passed through a static mixer, and then discharged toward the point of injection. A unit of this type is commercially available in the configuration as shown. The intent is to reduce viscosity and increase the velocity in the tubing or piping. The pump still controls the rate of chemical feed, while the dilution system reduces the potential for fouling and also makes it easier to mix the chemical with the process water at the point of injection. Methods of injection also will be discussed in this chapter.

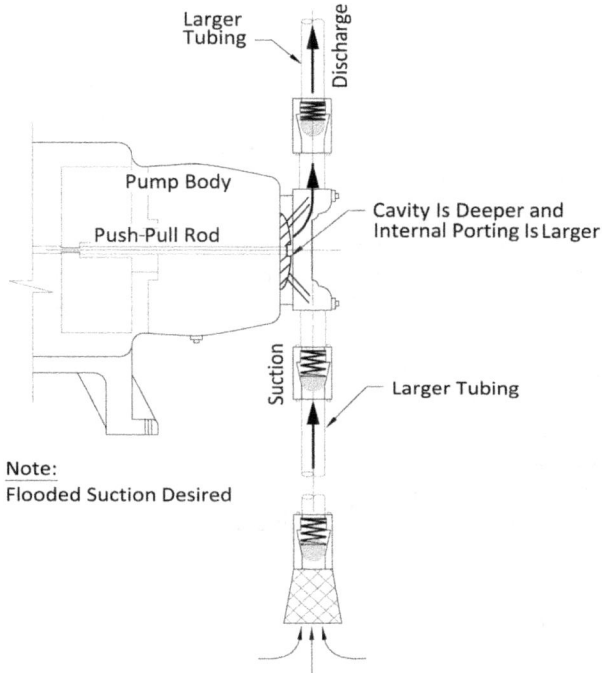

Figure 5-7   **Diaphragm pump viscous solutions**

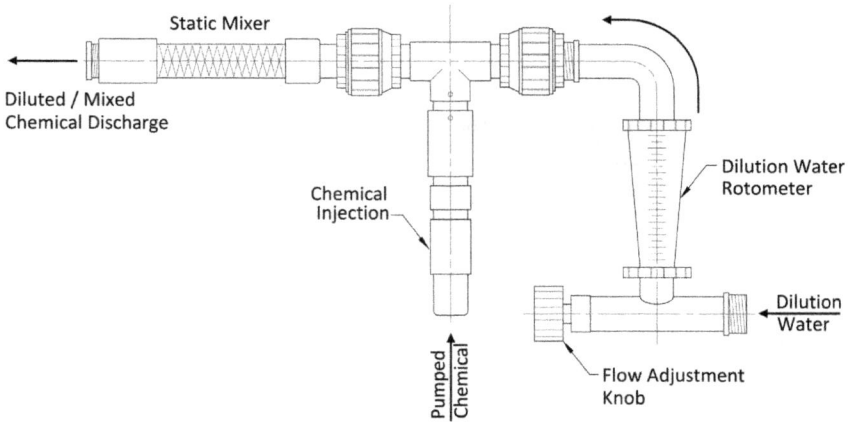

NOTE

Dilution Water Flow is Typically 2-5 gpm as a Minimum. Higher Flows are Better But May not be Practical on Smaller Systems.

Figure 5-8   **Polymer dilution/mixing system**

Peristaltic Pumps

A peristaltic pump is a simple positive-displacement pump using a rotary roller/lobe to compress the tubing and move the chemical forward. The operation of a peristaltic pump is illustrated in Figure 5-9. In the past, this type of pump was primarily used for instrumentation and laboratory purposes. In those cases, the pumps were very small, using very small tubing that in some cases was directional.

The problem with peristaltic pumps always has been the potential failure of the tubing after many compression/relaxation cycles. However, as a result of improved tubing types, larger peristaltic pumps are currently used successfully.

The advantage of this type of pump is that it is very simple and has few parts. To offset the potential problem of tubing failure, a long length of tubing is provided with the pump. The section of tubing actually being used in the pump is advanced periodically, resulting in longer life. Moving the tubing occasionally and following the manufacturer's instructions about replacement of the tubing have made this type of pump much more reliable.

1. SUCTION
The Roller First Compresses The Pump Hose, Occluding it Completely. As the Roller Moves on, the Hose Recovers its Initial Shape. This Creates the Necessary Suction to Draw in the Product.

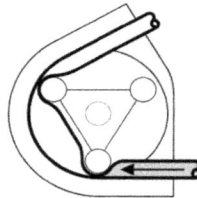

2. SUCTION
The Volume of Product Contained Between Two Rollers is Transferred Along the Hose From the Suction to the Delivery End.

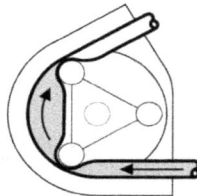

3. SUCTION
Under the Pressure of the Second Roller, the Product is Pumped into the Delivery Pipeline.

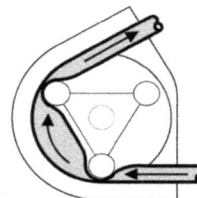

Figure 5-9   Peristaltic pump system

Progressive Cavity Pumps

A progressive cavity pump is illustrated in Figure 5-10. In this type of pump, the motor drives a rotor in the shape of a helix. A rubber stator is fixed to the side wall of the pump chamber and also has a helical molded shape. As the rotor turns, it progressively squeezes the material through the stator and discharges it out the end.

A progressive cavity pump is typically used for viscous fluids and some sludges. In some water treatment plants, it is used as the basic polymer pump. In this discussion, it is used as a transfer pump for polymers, as shown in Figure 5-11. A progressive cavity pump is not recommended for slurries or other abrasive materials. Abrasive materials cause very rapid wear to the stator, causing deterioration in operation. If there is any question regarding the application, the manufacturer should be consulted for a discussion of recommended uses.

Accessories

A schematic of a complete chemical system assembly is shown in Figure 5-12. In this figure, many of the common accessories are illustrated. A brief discussion of each is given in the following sections.

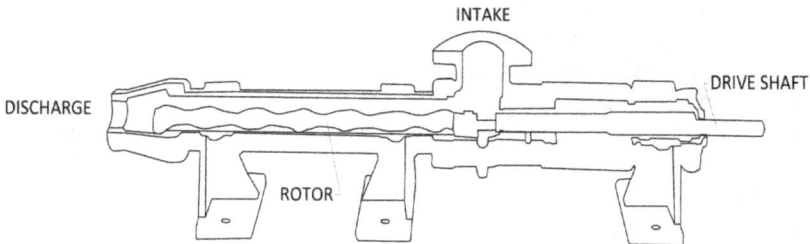

NOTES:

Positive Displacement:
   A Single Rotating Element Generates Positive Displacement Progressing Cavities Which Deliver Predictable, Uniform, Continuous Flow. Head is Independent of Speed. Slippage is a Function of Viscosity and Pressure.

Operation:
   The Key Components are the Rotor and the Stator. The Rotor is a Single External Helix with a Round Cross-Section. The Stator is a Double Internal Helix Molded of a Tough, Abrasion-Resistant Elastomer. As the Rotor Turns Within the Stator, Cavities are Formed Which Progress From the Suction to the Discharge End of the Pump Material.

Figure 5-10   Progressive cavity pumps

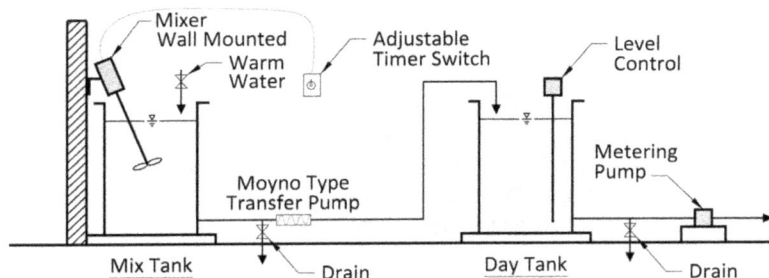

NOTES:

1. Mix Tank/Day Systems Are Typically Used For Hard-To-Mix Polymers Or In a Situation Where The Plant Cannot Be Shut Down For Long. A New Batch of Chemical can be Mixed Before the Day Tank Runs Out.

2. Automatic Systems Are Available For This Purpose, But The Equipment Shown Here Is Easier To Maintain, In The Author's Opinion.

3. The Mix Tank Is Usually Filled Manually With A Measured Amount Of Chemical Being Added

4. Warm Water Is Recommended For Mixing Purposes To Aid In Dissolving The Chemical

Figure 5-11   Polymer day tanks/mix tanks

Tanks

Chemicals can be delivered to the site in barrels, totes, or in bulk tank trucks. The container holding the chemicals being pumped can be the barrel it was delivered in, a standard plastic or fiberglass tank, a double-bottomed tank, a tote, or a bulk storage tank. A tote is a large square tank, which is typically delivered to the job site by the chemical manufacturer. Totes may have a capacity of 500 to 1,000 gallons. Tanks can vary from small plastic tanks to 10,000-gallon bulk storage tanks. Large treatment plants commonly use bulk storage tanks to allow for truck delivery of chemicals for reduced maintenance and handling purposes, as well as lower costs.

A small tank can be picked up and cleaned manually when empty. However, for 100-gallon tanks and larger, a drain on the lower sidewall is recommended to assist in cleaning and flushing. A connection on the lower sidewall is also recommended to provide pumps with a flooded suction, as mentioned previously. Smaller systems may pump directly out of a barrel. However, many chemicals in granular or powdered form need to be mixed prior to their use.

Mixers

Some chemicals are provided in a powder or granular form and require mixing with water prior to use. Other chemicals may be diluted prior to their use, while still others such as carbon and lime are fed in slurries, which require continuous mixing to keep the granular particles in solution. For very small systems, the mixers are often mounted on the top lid of the tank, while for larger systems the mixer may be mounted on the sidewall of the tank or an adjacent wall. Wall mounting is commonly used when the mixer is large enough to cause the tank to vibrate excessively. The manufacturer should be consulted for mounting recommendations.

The size and power required for mixing are typically dependent on the type of chemical to be used and the size of the tank. However, slow speed gear-driven mixers are preferred, especially when mixing polymers, so as not to tear apart the molecular structure of the chemical.

Valves

Multifunction valves (not shown). A multifunction valve is often provided directly on the discharge of the diaphragm chemical metering pump. One of the purposes of this valve is to assist in priming the pump prior to its operation. For additional information, the manufacturer should be consulted.

Backpressure valves. Because of the check valve arrangement shown previously for a diaphragm pump (Figures 5-2 and 5-3), the pump operates better when pumping against pressure. The amount of pressure required may vary with the pump, and the manufacturer should be consulted for additional information.

Some pumps will discharge directly to a high-pressure process pipe, while others will discharge to a gravity system with little backpressure. For those cases where the discharge pressure requirements are not high, a backpressure valve may be installed to create better operating conditions for the pump.

Pressure-relief valves. A diaphragm metering pump is a positive displacement type. If part of the system were to become fouled or a valve in the discharge line inadvertently closed, the pump would immediately produce its maximum pressure and could destroy part of the pump or rupture some of the fittings. As a result, it is common to provide a pressure-relief valve so that the pump can remain operating within its limits, while adequate flow to relieve pressure is routed back to the feed tank, as shown in Figure 5-11. In some cases, a pressure-relief function may be incorporated in the multifunction valve mentioned previously. In either case, a pressure-relief function is recommended.

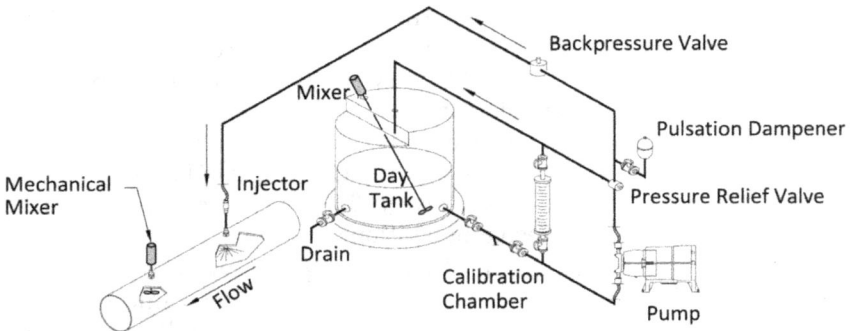

Figure 5-12   Chemical system assemblies

Calibration Chambers

Partial plugging, or the viscosity of the chemical, may cause diaphragm pumps to operate slower than the design rate. Therefore, a calibration chamber is commonly provided to allow periodic computation of the actual pumping rate. It is essentially a graduated cylinder that can be filled from the bottom, usually from the feed tank. The calibration chamber is allowed to fill from the chemical tank and then the valve from the tank is closed, allowing the pump to operate on the contents of the calibration chamber. The timed drawdown rate of chemical in the calibration chamber can then be used to determine the actual pumping rate for its speed and stroke settings. Periodic calculation of the actual pumping rate is an important maintenance function for each chemical system.

Pulsation Dampeners (Surge Suppressors)

Diaphragm pumps operate in pulses generated from each stroke. Especially with larger pumps, the pulse can be quite large. To even out the pump discharge, a pulsation dampener (surge suppressor) is often provided. The pulsation dampener is a small bladder tank that can absorb the pulses, resulting in smoother discharge of the chemicals.

Gauge Isolators (Not Shown)

When pressure gauges are required on a chemical system or on the chemically treated process water, it is often desirable to provide a *gauge isolator* to protect them from corrosion or plugging by the chemical. A gauge isolator is usually constructed of 316 stainless steel, or a type of plastic, and has a diaphragm that allows pressure to be transmitted to the gauge without allowing the chemical to come in contact with its internals. The use of gauge isolators is another function that can be provided that will reduce maintenance and allow better operation.

Flow Sensors

A *paddle-type* flow switch is often provided on chemical tubing/piping as an indication that the pump is actually operating. Such a device is recommended as an early warning of a potential failure, which may allow the operator to correct a situation before damage occurs.

Flowmeters

When it is possible for the process flow rate to change, it is usually desirable for the chemical pump to change rate with it. For that purpose, flowmeters (not shown) are often installed on the process pipe to control the speed of operation of the chemical pump. For that to work, the chemical pump is usually provided with a variable signal input capability such as 4–20 mA control. For small systems, the chemical pump manufacturer may provide a flowmeter to control the pump directly. On larger systems, the flowmeter may send a signal to the central control system, which in turn will transmit a variable control signal to the chemical pump. This method of control is common, especially if there is a considerable distance between the flowmeter and the chemical pump.

Flushing Systems

When using carbon and lime slurries, a flushing system is highly recommended. The intent is to prevent solids from being deposited in the diaphragm cavity of the pump or in the pipeline. An automatic system can be provided that injects clean water into the pump suction on an adjustable time basis, such as illustrated in Figure 5-13.

As an alternative, a manual system may be necessary to flush all the discharge piping periodically to prevent deposition of solids. A manual system is illustrated in Figure 5-14. The intent is to flush the entire line when the system shuts off to prevent the solids in the pipeline from settling out and compacting. Compacted solids may be difficult to refluidize. A system of this type can also be made automatic to reduce operational requirements by installing two solenoid valves.

The effect of a complete flush, such as previously described, is that instead of the tubing or piping being full of chemical when the unit starts up, it will take a period of time for the newly pumped chemical

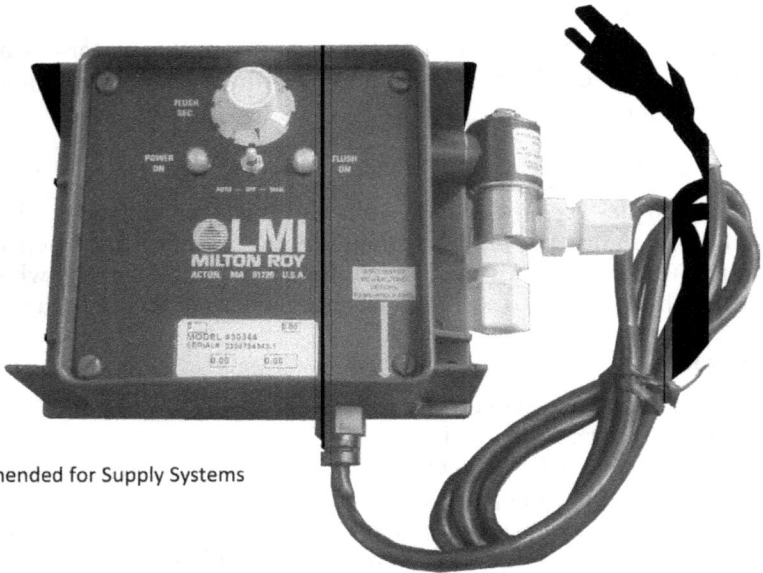

NOTE:
Recommended for Supply Systems

Courtesy of Milton Roy America and Liquid Metronics (LMI)

Figure 5-13   Automatic flushing system

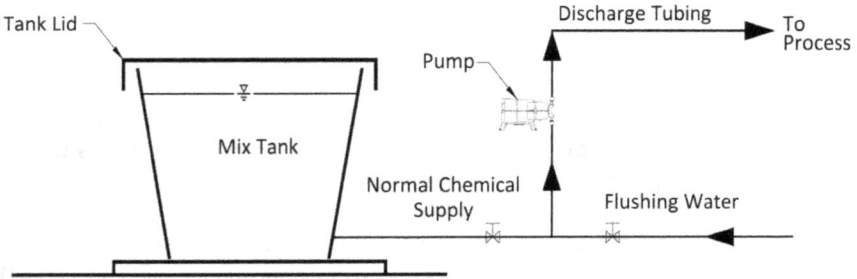

NOTE:
1. Wait for Plant to Turn Off.
2. Close Valve to Normal Chemical Supply.
3. Open Valve to Flushing Water.
4. Turn Pump Controls to Manual Operation.
5. Operate in Manual Mode Long Enough to flush Entire
   Length of Discharge Tubing / Piping.
6. Return All Components to Normal Position.

Figure 5-14   Manual flushing

to reach the point of injection. In that case, a time delay may be built into the control system for more efficient operation.

Injection Quills

The author has observed applications where the chemical pump discharges directly to the process pipe through a threaded coupling. If that is the case, PVC or HDPE pipe is recommended at that point. Directly injecting some chemicals such as chlorine will cause significant corrosion in steel pipe and in the fittings.

Figure 5-11 illustrates an injector assembly where the chemical is introduced into the process pipeline. An *injection quill* is recommended for larger applications. In Figure 5-15, the quill can be adjusted so that it discharges chemical in the center of the pipe, which also assists in mixing the chemical with the process water. Also, this assembly allows withdrawal of the injection quill without shutting down the process system.

Flash Mixing

After the point of injection, it is highly recommended that some form of mixing take place to ensure complete dispersion of the chemical into the process flow. In Figure 5-12, a mechanical mixer is shown, and is recommended by the author for most applications. However, if the process flow is uniform or nearly so at all times, a static mixer may be used. A static mixer is a section of pipe with a series of vanes

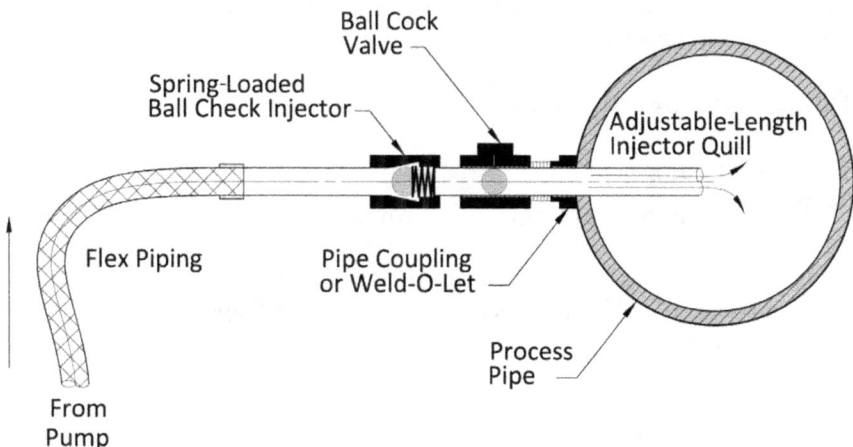

Figure 5-15   Injector assembly

designed to mix the flow. Flash mixing will be discussed in more detail later on in this chapter.

Materials of Construction

When specifying a pump, valves, or other accessories, it is important to choose the wetted parts such that they are compatible with the chemical being used. A chemical resistance chart is included in the Appendix. Chemical pump manufacturers typically maintain chemical resistance charts and will assist in selection of the proper pump components.

If it is chemically compatible, then an acrylic pump head is recommended for visibility. Maintenance on the pump will be simpler if any potential pluggage can be detected by observing it through the acrylic head.

Containment/Storage

When corrosive or other hazardous liquid chemicals are used, the storage tank may need to be isolated or contained. When leaks or ruptures in a chemical tank occur, the contents of the tank should be contained to prevent contamination of the building or other system components without endangering personnel. Containment may be provided by a double bottom tank or by installing the regular tank within a concrete tank. In case of a leak, the contents of the containment tank can be pumped out and removed safely.

When storing hazardous dry chemicals, a special cabinet or secure storage space may be required to isolate and protect the chemicals from a fire or a fire sprinkler system. For storage or containment of either liquid or dry chemicals, local regulatory authorities should be consulted for safety requirements.

Pump Rate Calculations

Diaphragm Pumps

Chemical pumps are normally provided with a separate 0 to 100 percent control dial for both speed and stroke. The capacity is normally rated on an hourly or daily production basis. The actual rate being produced is the product of the stroke and speed settings. An example follows:

Assumed pump capacity – 100 gpd
Assumed stroke – 50%
Assumed speed – 75%

Actual pump rate   = stroke × speed × pump capacity
                   = 0.5 × 0.75 × 100 gpd
                   = 37.5 gpd

Minimum and Maximum Rates

It is recommended that a chemical pump not be operated lower than 10 percent or higher than 90 percent on either the stroke or speed settings for a conservative design (also refer to the manufacturer).

1. Minimum pump capacity
    10% stroke × 10% speed = 0.01 × capacity

2. Maximum pump capacity
    90% stroke × 90% speed = 0.81 × rated capacity

For viscous polymers, the actual maximum rate may be lower, as previously discussed.

Sample Chemical Pump Sizing Calculations

1. Assumptions
    - Process Flow Rate = 600 gpm (0.86 mgd)
    - Chemical Used = Soda Ash (maximum solubility = 12% or 1 lb/gal)
    - Soda Ash Concentration Used = 6% (half of maximum to mitigate calcification)
    - Desired Soda Ash Feed Rate (for this example) = 4 mg/L (determined from jar testing for actual applications)

** Note: Design the chemical pump rate in terms of continuous maximum flow, even if the plant does not run 24 hours per day.

2. Calculations
    Chemical pump
    Flow rate $= \dfrac{\text{plant flow (mgd)} \times \text{chemical feed rate (mg/L)}}{\text{mix concentration}}$

    Flow rate $= \dfrac{0.86 \text{ mgd} \times 4 \text{ mg/L}}{0.06}$

            = 57.3 gpd

3. Pump Size Selection: Assumed Pump Sizes Available
    *   60 gpd
    *   96 gpd
    *   192 gpd

A capacity of 60 gpd would satisfy the rate calculated in the previous example but would not have any reserve capacity. It would also be above the recommended maximum rate of 81 percent (48.6 gpd). It is recommended that the design feed rate be approximately 50 percent of the pump capacity to allow for conditions exceeding the design conditions.

A 96-gpd pump would have a reserve capacity, which would provide the ability to deliver 5.4 mg/L of soda ash. (The design rate is 4 mg/L in the previous example.)

Minimum feed rate   = 0.067 mg/L (at 10%)
Maximum feed rate   = 5.4 mg/L (at 90% stroke and speed)

A 192-gpd pump would have a much higher reserve capacity, while still having an acceptable minimum.

Minimum feed rate   = 0.13 mg/L
Maximum feed rate   = 10.8 mg/L

Recommendation

Because of the normal (assumed) 100:1 turn-down capability, the 192-gpd pump is recommended. It can be turned down to a low rate to meet any probable minimum, while retaining the capability to provide additional capacity if desired.

Using the selected 192-gpd pump, the stroke and speed settings could be calculated as follows:

Desired pump rate   = 57.3 gpd (from paragraph 2)

57.3 gpd   = pump capacity (192 gpd) × stroke × speed

Stroke/speed $= \dfrac{57.3}{192}$

= 0.3 (30% of total capacity)

Stroke/speed   = 54% each (if equal)

Or: = 50%/60%

Installation

Small Systems

A small chemical feed assembly is illustrated in Figure 5-16. This diagram is typical of chemical tanks in the 35- to 50-gallon range. Tanks, 100 gallons and larger, are typically arranged differently, as will be discussed in the following section.

In Figure 5-14, both the pump and the mixer are often mounted to the tank lid. The flexible discharge tubing must be long enough to allow the lid to be removed without disassembling the pump. To keep the suction tubing from becoming fouled in the mixer, a *suction tube shield* is installed in the tank, consisting of a PVC pipe with holes drilled for venting. It is usually attached to the bottom of the tank lid on small tanks. The suction tubing is then inserted into the suction tube shield with a ceramic weight to keep the suction check valve and strainer near the bottom.

Installing the pump in this manner requires a small amount of suction lift. In most cases, this is acceptable. However, in a warm environment, there may be problems with vapor lock, especially when pumping liquid chlorine. The chlorine can easily vaporize in a suction situation, causing the pump to lose its prime. Viscous polymers may also have similar problems, because of the weight and resistance of the chemical. One solution would be to dilute the chemical prior to use. An alternative would be to modify the tank as shown in Figure 5-15 for larger systems.

Larger Systems (100-Gallon Tanks and Larger)

In larger systems, a chemical tank may be so heavy that it cannot reasonably be moved once it is installed. It may also be so tall that it creates a suction lift problem when the level is low and the pump is mounted on the lid or above the tank. Therefore, a bulkhead fitting, or molded fitting, is recommended on the lower sidewall of the tank for drain purposes and for suction tubing to the pump. In Figure 5-17, the pump is shown above the tank, requiring a suction lift. In most cases, this is *not* desirable. When there is a lower tank connection, the pump should be installed on or near the floor to ensure flooded suction.

At least 3 feet of flexible tubing is recommended on the suction and discharge side of the pump to prevent damage to the pipeline, as mentioned previously. A calibration chamber would be difficult to use with the pump above the tank, as shown here. However, if the pump were installed on or near the floor, a calibration chamber would work well.

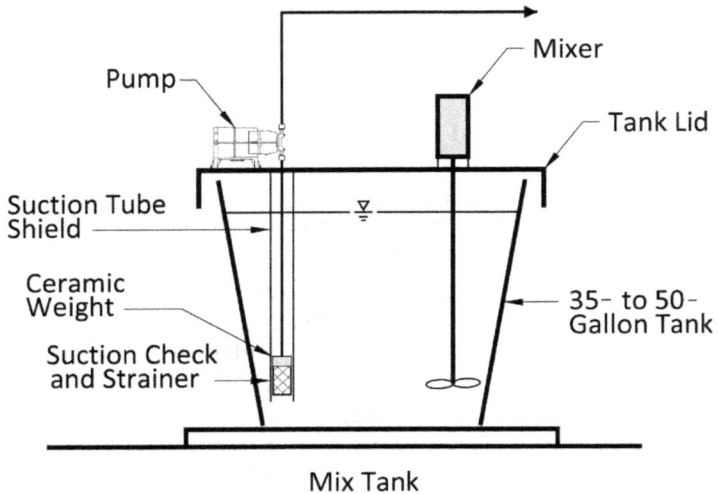

NOTE: Mix Tank

Larger Systems Will Have The Mixer Mounted to the Tank or Building
    Wall, While the Pump May be Wall or Floor Mounted.

Figure 5-16   Small pump and mix tank assemblies

Mix Tank/Day Tank Chemical Systems

Cationic polymers are typically provided in a bulk liquid form and
are often pumped neat (undiluted), especially where the distance to
the point of injection is short. On the other hand, the author has witnessed several installations where the chemical pumps were actually
too big for the system and the chemicals were diluted to allow for
proper operation. Dilution may also be necessary for small systems to
allow a small pump to operate at the desired capacity.

Anionic polymers are typically provided in a dry granular form and
must be dissolved prior to use. Anionic polymers are often difficult to
mix, and a system such as shown in Figure 5-11 is recommended for
mixing dry polymers, as well as diluting other chemicals.

In Figure 5-11, dry chemical is measured into the mix tank (pref-
erably with warm water), and the mixer may be set to run for several
hours using an adjustable timer switch. In this case, the system does
not require an operator to be present during the mixing cycle. Once
the chemical is mixed properly, a progressive cavity-type pump can
be used to transfer the chemical to the day tank. In this way, the
system can remain in operation without being taken off line to mix
chemicals. Automatic systems for mixing dry polymers are available,
but the system shown is simpler and may be more reliable.

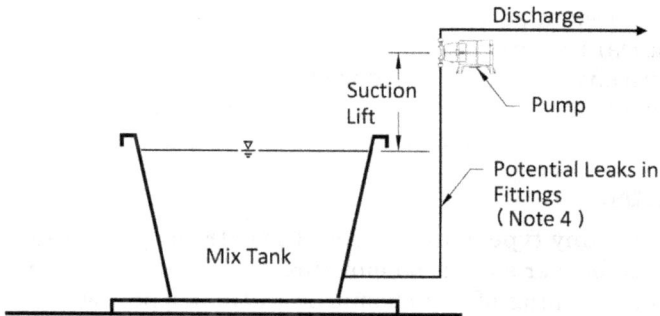

NOTES:

1. Having a Short Suction Lift May Work For Some Chemicals. However, the Lower The Chemical Level, the Greater the Lift.

2. A Suction Lift on Some Chemicals, Such as Liquid Chlorine, May Cause Gas to Come Out of Solution and Result in Loss of Prime.

3. Heavy, Viscous Polymers and Chlorine Should Have a Flooded Suction.

4. Leaks in the Fittings on the Suction Side of the Pump can Also Result in Loss of Prime.

Figure 5-17   Pump Installation

A system similar to this can be used for diluting chlorine or other chemicals if required. For diluting chlorine, the chemical is typically pumped from a barrel to the day tank using a drum-type pump. Mixing is rapid, and a separate tank may not be required.

Dry Feeders

Dry chemicals are often delivered to large treatment plants in bulk trucks to reduce material costs. The dry chemicals are then stored in a large hopper. A rotary scalloped feeder at the bottom of the hopper discharges a metered amount of chemical into the system for use, as illustrated in Figure 5-18. Dry feeders are often used for soda ash, lime, and sometimes potassium permanganate although with a much smaller hopper. Smaller dry feeder systems are also used to feed anionic polymers.

In a dry feeder of this type, the feed rate is set by varying the speed of the scalloped positive-displacement rotor in the bottom of the hopper, as shown in Figure 5-18. The dry chemical is then dropped into a tank of water where a mixer runs continuously. A constant-speed centrifugal pump is typically used to deliver the mixed chemical to the process stream, while a float system is used to control the flow of makeup water to match the pump discharge and to maintain a constant volume in the mix tank.

Potassium permanganate is a very fine powder. When using that chemical in a dry feeder, the equipment must be properly designed to prevent slippage of the dry chemical past the rotor when it is not in operation and to prevent a larger than desired volume of chemical from passing through the system.

Vibrators

With any type of dry feeder, it is extremely important to seal the storage hopper so that no moisture enters. Moisture can cause bridging or clumping of dry chemicals in the hopper, which prevents the powder from being properly fed by the rotary feeder. A vibrator is often attached to the hopper to mitigate bridging.

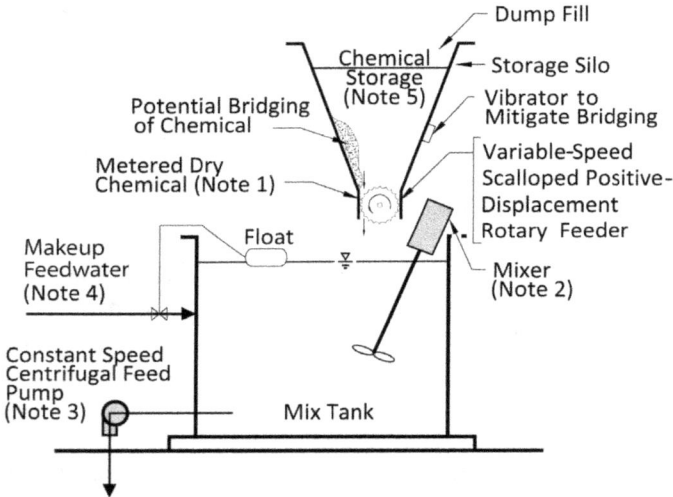

NOTES:
1. Depending On The Chemical Used And The Design Of The Feeder. Assembly, Some Slippage Of Chemical Past The Feeder Is Possible.
2. The Mixer Runs Continuously While Chemical Is Being Fed.
3. The Feed Pump Is Sized To Pump The Mixed Chemical Fast Enough So That The Solubility Limit Of The Chemical Is Not Reached At The Maximum Feed Rate.
4. A Float- Or Level-Controlled Supply Of Clean Water Is Provided To Match The Pumped Discharge From The Tank And Maintain A Constant Volume.
5. The Storage Hopper Must Be Covered And Sealed To Prevent Moisture From Causing The Formation Of Lumps Or Bridging Of The Chemical.

Figure 5-18   Dry feeders

Pump Sizing

The following calculations are included to determine the pumping rate for a dry system. It should be noted that the calculations show a minimum pump rate to be maintained, while a larger pump would be more desirable. The speed of the pump has no impact on the amount of chemical delivered to the system. The intent of the feed pump is to keep the solution dilute enough so that no calcification or buildup of undissolved chemical takes place in the tank, pump, or discharge tubing.

Pump Sizing for Dry Feeders

1. Assumptions:

Process flow rate	= 2 mgd
Feed rate	= 3 mg/L
Maximum mix concentration desired	= 6% by weight
	= 0.5 lb/gal

2. Calculations:

   Feed rate (by weight) = 3 mg/L × 2 mgd × 8.33 lb/gal
   = 50 lbs/day

   Solution strength = 0.06 (from above)

   Minimum flow rate = $\dfrac{3 \text{ mg/L} \times 2 \text{ mgd}}{0.06}$

   Or:

   = $\dfrac{50 \text{ lb/day}}{0.5 \text{ lb/gal}}$

   = 100 gal/day

   = 0.07 gpm minimum pump rate

** Note: The pumping rate is intended to be high enough to prevent the chemical concentration from exceeding the 6 percent limit for soda ash. Higher flow rates could be used and are recommended but not lower rates.

Fluoride Feeders/Saturators

1.   Liquid. Fluoride can be obtained as a liquid (fluosilicic acid) or in a dry granular form, as sodium fluoride. Fluosilicic acid is highly corrosive and is typically pumped neat to the process water. Other than using pipe and pump fittings that are chemically compatible, the other major concern with feeding the liquid form is that the tank will most likely require containment. Local regulatory authorities should be consulted about containment and the equipment manufacturer should be consulted about compatibility of materials for the pump, tank, and discharge pipe.

2.   Sodium fluoride (dry). The solid form of fluoride requires somewhat more operational attention but is simpler to use overall, especially for smaller systems.
     Rather than mix the solid fluoride in the tank, a fluoride saturator is typically used, as shown in Figure 5-19. Fluoride is emptied from bags into the saturator manually. The inlet water enters the bottom of the tank through a distributor and flows up through the solid fluoride material, and the liquid becomes 100 percent saturated. As the pump takes chemical out of the tank, a float assembly provides fresh makeup water to maintain a constant level. The intent is to continuously maintain a saturated fluoride concentration in the tank at all times. The maximum saturation level is approximately 4 percent by weight.
     It should be noted that to ensure proper solubility, it is recommended that the inlet water first be treated with a softener to remove hardness. Otherwise, the fluoride may not dissolve as intended. Therefore, it is recommended that a softener be considered as standard equipment with a fluoride saturator. The maximum effective feed rate of fluoride is considered to be one part per million.

Process Mixing

Direct Injection

When chemicals are injected into a process stream, the intent is for them to be thoroughly and uniformly mixed with the process flow as quickly as possible. Injecting the chemical through a half coupling in the side of the pipe is called *direct injection*. Complete mixing is difficult to achieve in this case and can lead to corrosion of the process pipe at the point of injection. The author has witnessed numerous

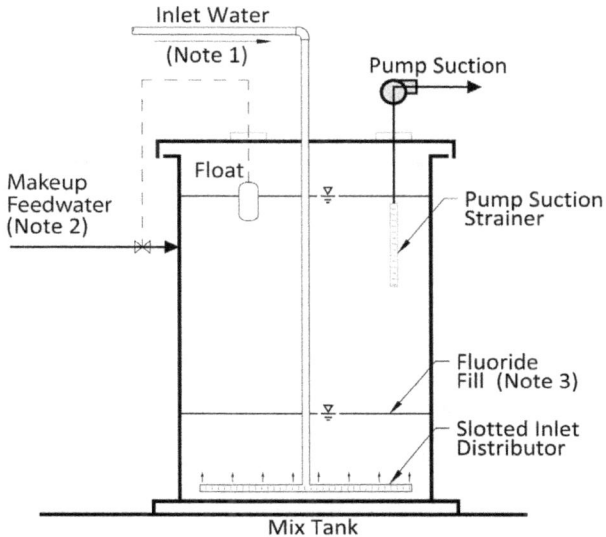

NOTES:
1. Float-Controlled Valve Maintains Constant Water Level.
2. Inlet Flow Is Recommended To Be Slow And Steady To Prevent Fluoride Solids From Fluidizing.
3. Fluoride Is Added As Needed.

Figure 5-19   Fluoride saturator

cases where corrosion of steel pipe has been so extensive as to cause the half coupling to fall off.

Figure 5-20 illustrates both direct injection and the uniform mixing that is desired. However, direct injection does not normally result in uniform mixing unless there is a long length of pipeline afterward. Direct chemical injection is more likely to achieve the result illustrated in Figure 5-21. The chemical tends to stay close to the sidewall of the pipe, unless there is a considerable length of pipe or a number of bends or fittings downstream that can achieve complete mixing. Two examples of direct injection from actual installations are shown in Figure 5-22. In Example A, the piping splits shortly after the chemical was injected in the sidewall of the pipe, resulting in more of the chemical going to the right toward Filter 2 than to the left. A similar example is shown in Example B, where the filters on the right side of the diagram tend to get more chemical than those on the left. An uneven distribution of chemical is obviously very likely to result in uneven or inadequate treatment.

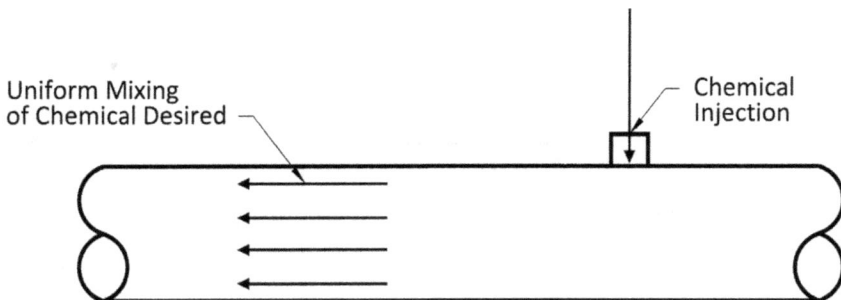

NOTE
The Intent of Injecting a Chemical is That it be Thoroughly and Uniformly
Mixed With the Process Flow as Quickly as Possible.

Figure 5-20   Desired mixing

Injection Quill

An injection quill was discussed previously and is illustrated in
Figure 5-15 and Figure 5-23. The use of an injector quill improves
mixing and protects the process pipe; even so, it is not normally adequate for complete mixing on its own, as illustrated in Figure 5-22.

As previously discussed, chemical dilution at the feed pump aids
in mixing chemicals in the process stream more rapidly, especially
for polymers. Additional mixing is normally required.

Flexible Tubing

Flexible tubing is recommended on either side of a diaphragm pump
and next to the injector. Because diaphragm pumps operate in a pulsation mode, continued vibration can cause cracking of the chemical
discharge pipe. Therefore, if rigid piping is used, a 2- to 3-foot section of
flexible tubing is recommended in those locations to protect the pipe.

In some cases, there is a significant difference as to which chemical is injected first. For that purpose, it is recommended that at least
10 feet of flexible tubing be provided at the point of injection to allow
the injector quill to be moved to another location if required.

Flash Mixing

Rapid or flash mixing is recommended at the point of injection
of any chemical, as discussed previously. The purpose is to evenly
distribute the chemical in the process water and increase the

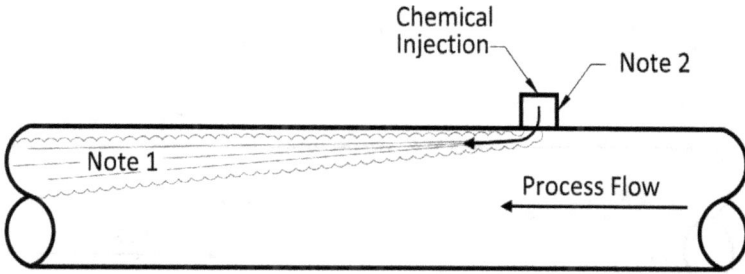

NOTES

1. The Chemical Tends to Stay Close to the Pipe of Conduit Sidewall. A Considerable Length of the Pipe or a Number of Bends or Pipe Fittings are Required to Achieve Complete Mixing.

2. Injecting the Chemical Directly into the Sidewall of the Pipe of Conduit can Lead to Rapid Corrosion, Depending on the Chemical Used.

Figure 5-21 Direct chemical injection

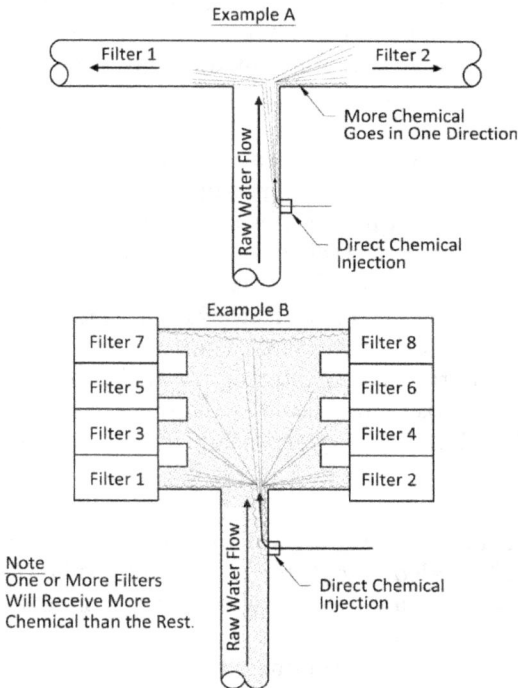

Figure 5-22 Direct injection

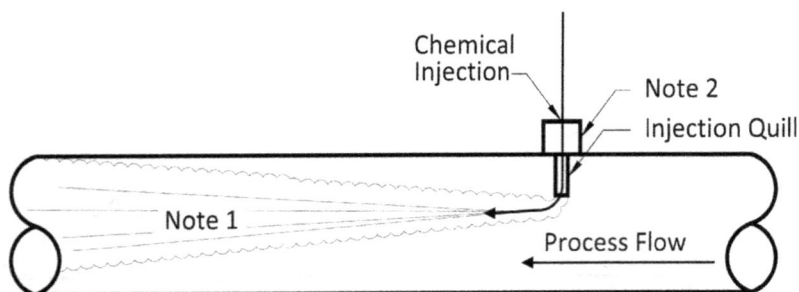

NOTES
1. The Plume of Chemical Spreads out More Quickly than Direct Injection, but Still Takes a Long Distance to Achieve Complete Mixing.
2. The Use of an Injection Quill Greatly Reduces the Potential for Corrosion of the Sidewall.

Figure 5-23   Injection quill

effectiveness of the chemical. An energy input of about 3 feet of water pressure is recommended in a short period of time.

Mechanical mixers and static mixers can achieve flash mixing. A mechanical mixer is shown in Figure 5-24 and is recommended for most applications, because the mixing intensity does not go down with reductions in process flow rate. A static mixer, as shown in Figure 5-25, consists of a pipe section with a series of mixing vanes. Different manufacturers have different designs for the mixing vanes, and they can be made of PVC or stainless steel. The chemical injection is usually in the body of the mixer, as shown. The recommended energy input is about 3 feet of water pressure head loss. However, for a static mixer the mixing intensity varies with the square of the pipe velocity. If the process flow is reduced by half, the mixing intensity would be reduced by 75 percent. Therefore, static mixers are recommended for those applications where the process flow does not vary appreciably.

Weirs

Mixing with water flow over weirs or in a hydraulic jump, as shown in Figure 5-26, is also acceptable if available. When using a weir, it is recommended that a spray bar with a series of nozzles be installed across the channel to more evenly distribute the flow of chemical. In this case, dilution is also recommended to increase the volume so that the nozzles will operate more efficiently. Diluted chemicals will also mix faster.

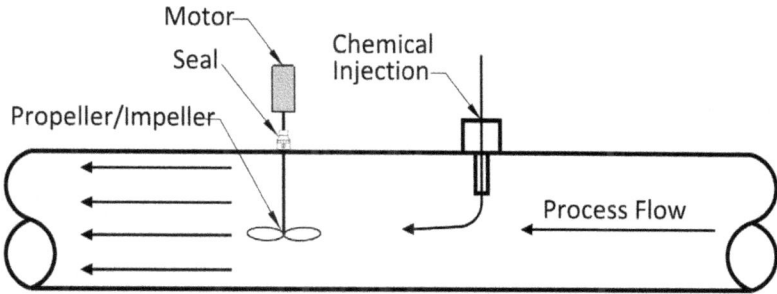

NOTES

1. Recommended Energy Input Should be Approximately 3 Feet of Head loss.

2. Motor Size and Mixing Intensity Vary Depending on Pipe Size, Process Flow, and The Chemicals Being Used.

3. Provides the Same Power Input at Any Flow.

Figure 5-24   Mechanical flash mixer

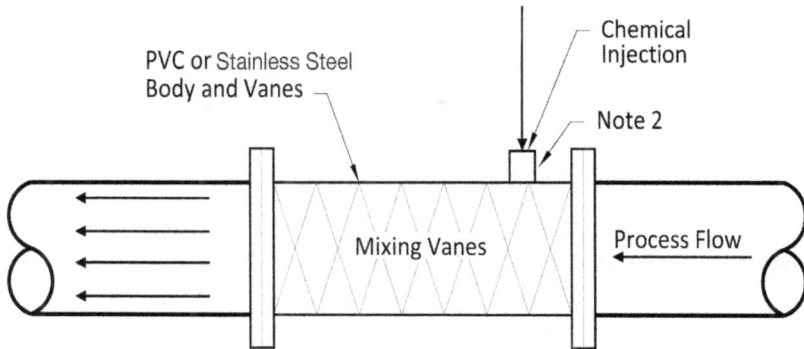

NOTES

1. Recommended Energy Input Should be Approximately 3 Feet of Head loss.

2. Head loss and Mixing Efficiency Will be Flow Dependent.

Figure 5-25   Static mixer

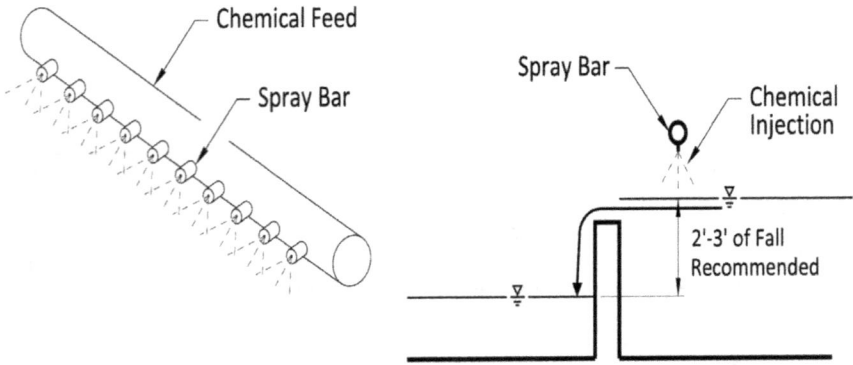

NOTES

1. Not Recommended for Chlorine Due to the Potential for Off-Gassing.

2. The Spray Bar Should be Suspended Across the Length of the Weir with a Series of Nozzles or Orifices. Pressurized Dilution Water Should be Used to Distribute the Chemical as Equally as Possible.

Figure 5-26   Flow over weir chemical injection

Chemical Monitoring

On-line chemical monitors are recommended before and after chemical addition, and also after treatment at the point of discharge into the distribution system. Although not discussed extensively, the following comments are offered for the operator's use.

A rapid response time between a change in chemical feed and a change recorded by the monitor is important to plant operation. Therefore, it is highly recommended that the monitor be close to the sample point so that any process changes will be recorded as soon as possible. Also, high loops in the sample line should be avoided, if possible. There is less chance for the sample in chlorine feed systems to vaporize or for other chemical reactions to occur when the system is off line.

Process Problems and Solutions

Description of Problem	Potential Causes	Possible Resolution
Loss of prime/won't stay primed	Loose suction side fittings	Inspect all fittings and tighten as required
	Plugged or fouled suction tubing	Inspect/clean suction strainer (if used)
		Flush suction tubing/pipe
		Disassemble check valves and clean
		Ensure that check valves are installed properly
		Disassemble pump head and clean cavity and internal porting
	Inadequately mixed chemical	Mix longer Dilute chemical
	Too high a suction lift (if applicable)	Previous issues are all applicable
		Chlorine: a. Install bulkhead fitting on tank and lower pump
		or b. Dilute chemical
		or c. Both a and b (best)
		Polymer:
		a. Same as above
		b. Provide larger pump with the proper head for viscous solutions
	Cracking/breakage of rigid suction/ discharge piping	Install flexible suction/discharge tubing

Description of Problem	Potential Causes	Possible Resolution
Delamination/tearing of diaphragm	Normal wear	Replace diaphragm
	Abrasive solids buildup	Clean head
Pump stalling (operating but not pumping)	Discharge line plugged	Flush with warm water
		Install dilution assembly after pump
	Delamination/tearing of diaphragm	Same as above
	Polymer pump operating at high speed	Slow down pump
		Provide bigger pump and/or dilute chemical
	Backpressure valve malfunction or set too high	Readjust valve
		Provide new valve
Erratic residual chlorine after injection	Inadequate process mixing	Add/increase mixing after chemical injection
Erratic pH after chemical injection	Same	
Treatment results don't match jar tests	Investigate temperature effects of testing or treatment	
	Verify the accuracy of testing procedures (±10% is good)	
	Plant flow not as calculated	Provide new flowmeter
		Recalibrate existing flowmeter

Specialized Problems	Potential Causes	Solutions
Dry feeders, mix tank, pump, or discharge piping fouled	Feed pump too small	Check pump sizing calculations
		Flush with chemical cleaner
		Provide larger discharge pump
	Makeup water too cold	Use warmer mix water
		Use much larger pump and keep mix tank dilution lower
Fluoride saturator feed concentration too low	Lack of softener	Provide softener
	Softener resin fouled	Chemically clean or replace resin
	Makeup water too cold	Provide warmer water, if possible
	Saturator too small	Provide larger unit

Comments

1. Loss of prime is the most common cause of chemical pump failure, as seen by the number of issues that can cause the condition. Once the chemical feed system is set up properly, this problem should not reoccur unless the suction tubing becomes fouled or broken.

2. Most chemical pumps have a 100:1 turn-down capability. The capacity range of the pump should be suitable to meet the system needs in all conditions.

3. There can be a solids residue in some liquid chemicals. Therefore, the feed tank pump and tubing should be flushed periodically as a routine part of the maintenance program. Strainers on the suction tubing may also be needed. However, they are not recommended for use with viscous polymers.

4. Another advantage in having a length of clear tubing at the discharge point is to determine if the chemical is moving as desired.

There may be an air bubble that can be watched for movement, or slurry grains may have movement caused by the pulsing motion of the pump.

5. Larger discharge tubing may be needed if the system is changed so that a more dilute chemical is used or if a dilution panel is added to the pump discharge.

6. If a new pump is not working properly, everything should be checked and no assumptions made. The author has witnessed at least one incident where a large new chemical pump did not operate properly because one of its check valves was installed backward at the factory.

7. Recalibrate the pump at several speeds after all repairs and routine maintenance tasks have been completed.

Recommended Maintenance

1. A graduated cylinder should be used to verify the pumping rate of each chemical pump at least once a week. If the pumping rate varies substantially from past calculations, the head should be taken apart, and the inside of the pump head should be cleaned and the valves checked.

2. The diaphragm and seals in the pump should be replaced yearly or as recommended by the manufacturer.

3. Maintain a spare parts kit for each type of pump in case of failure. A typical spare parts kit is shown in Figure 5-27, and includes a diaphragm and spare O-rings and gaskets for a complete replacement.

4. If economically feasible, it is recommended that spare pumps also be available on site in case of an emergency. However, the operator must be careful that the substitute pump has wetted parts suitable for the application.

Summary

Chemical feed pumps, injection methods, and mixing are an important part of most water systems. As with any other type of equipment, chemical feed equipment must be designed, installed and operated properly for optimum results.

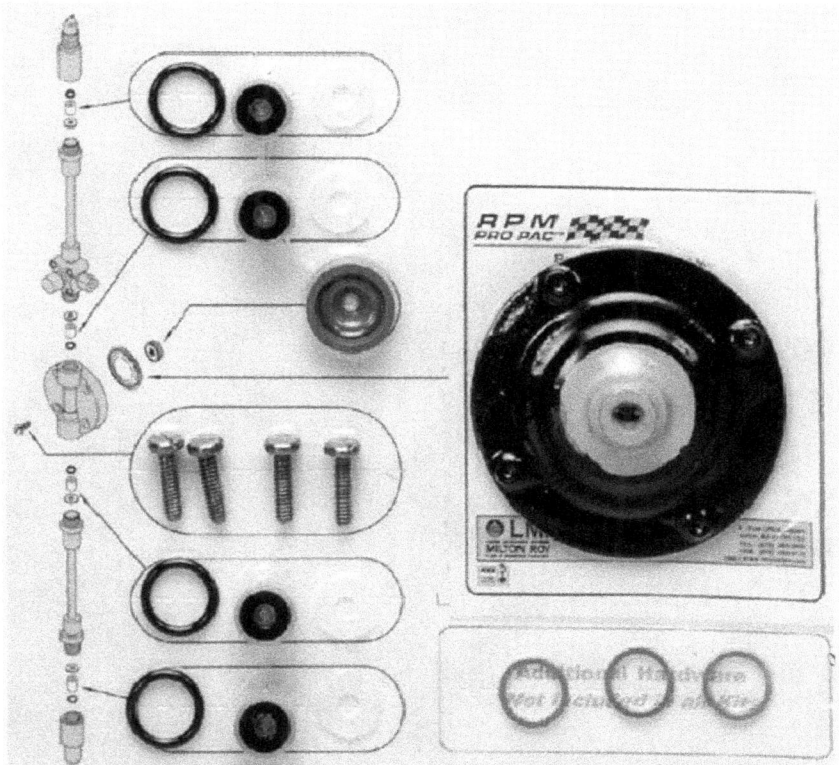

Figure 5-27   Diaphragm pump spare parts K17

CHAPTER 6

Operation and Maintenance Manual

On-Site Records

It is recommended that a copy of the following reference information be kept on site, including design data, for each pump:

Process Pumps

1. A flow diagram showing the basic components of the system

2. Design conditions
   - Pressure calculations
   - Elevation rise from pump (static pressure)
   - Suction-side pressure
   - Head loss due to pipe friction and fittings (valves, etc.)
   - Flow rate
   - Inlet conditions (suction pressure or suction lift)

3. Process pump description
   - Manufacturer
   - Model number
   - Number of stages (if applicable)
   - Horsepower
   - Rpm
   - Motor size and voltage

4. The family of curves and impeller size/curve

Chemical Pumps
   - Chemical to be pumped
   - Assumed chemical dilution or concentration
   - Design pump rate
   - Pump capacity and pressure

- Materials of construction
- Chemical compatibility

Maintenance Requirements

1. Manufacturer's recommendations

2. Scheduled maintenance
   - Weekly
   - Monthly
   - Annually

3. Maintenance checklist to show work done previously, as well as scheduled work to occur in the future

Spare Parts

1. An inventory of critical spare parts (diaphragm for each chemical pump, for example)

Accessories

The operator/owner should ensure that each pump (whether process or chemical feed) has the necessary accessories, including pressure gauges, flow meters, or calibration cylinders. In a proper installation, it should then be much easier for the pumps to be maintained.

Written Procedure

A brief written description is recommended to assist O&M personnel in evaluating each pump, including using pressure and/or flow, and its impeller curve to determine if the pump is operating as designed.

Chemical Resistance Chart

Material Definitions

Fluorofilm™ - a PTFE/PFA (perflouroalkoxy) copolymer
PTFE - polytetrafluoroethylene
PVDF - carbon fiber reinforced polyvinylidene fluoride
Polyprel® (AFLAS™) - an elastomeric copolymer of PTFE and propylene
Flexiprene™ (Santoprene®) - a thermoplastic elastomer vulcanizate
PVC - polyvinyl chloride
Viton® - a fluoroelastomer
Hypalon® - a chlorosulfonated polyethylene
Hastelloy® C - a nickle-based, corrosion-resistant metal alloy*

Note
*For applications where Hastelloy® C springs are not compatible, PVDF coated springs are available.

Note
For unlisted chemicals, consult factory.

Solution Temperature Maximum

For liquid handling components of LMI metering pumps operating at 100 psi (6.9 Bar)

Material	Example of Use	Temperature	
		°F	°C
PVDF (Carbon Fiber Reinforced)	Fittings and Pump Head	250*	121*
Polyprel® (AFLAS®)	Seal Rings	250*	121*
Polypropylene	Fittings and Pump Head	170	77
Polyvinyl Chloride Rigid (PVC)	Fittings and Pump Head	140	60
Polyvinyl Chloride (Flexible Vinyl)	Suction Tubing	140	60
Polyethylene	Discharge Tubing	110	43
Acrylic	Pump Head	140	60
PTFE	Liquifram™ and Seal Rings	250*	121*
Hypalon®	Diaphragm and Seal Rings	225	107
Viton®	Diaphragm and Seal Rings	225	107
Stainless Steel (316)	Fittings and Pump Head	250*	121*
Copolymer PTFE	Liquifram™	250*	121*
Hastelloy® C	Springs	250*	121*
Flexiprene™ (Santoprene®)	Uni-Valve™ and Flapper	212	100
EPDM	Seal Rings	225	107
CPVC	Pipe, Corp Stop	180	82
BUNA-N	Gasket, Corp Stop	220	104

* Limited by other pump components

Chemical or Solution	Hastelloy® C	PTFE/Fluorofilm™	PVDF	Polyprel® (AFLAS™)	Flexiprene™	Polypropylene	PVC	Stainless Steel (316)	Acrylic	Polyethylene	Viton®	Hypalon®	Vinyl	NOTES
Acetaldehyde	1	1	1	2	1	2	3	1	3	2	1	3	3	⚠
Acetic Acid, Glacial	1	1	1	3	3	1	3	2	3	3	3	2	3	⚠
Acetic Acid, 5%	1	1	1	3	1	1	1	1	1	1	1	2		
Acetic Anhydride	1	1	3	2	1	3	3	1	3	3	3	1	3	⚠
Acetone	1	1	2	3	2	1	3	1	3	3	3	2	3	⚠
Acetyl Chloride	1	1	2		1	1	1	1	3	3	1	3	3	⚠
Acrylonitrile	1	1	2	2		1		1	3	3	2	3		⚠
Adipic Acid		1	1		1	1	1	1	1	1			1	
Allyl Alcohol		1	1		1	1	2	1	3	3	2		2	⚠
Alcohol, Amyl	1	1	1	2	2	1	1	1	3	3	1	1	2	⚠
Alcohol, Benzyl	1	1	2	3	2	1	3	1	3	3	1	1	3	⚠
Alcohol, Butyl	1	1	1	1	1	2	2	1	3	3	1	1	2	⚠
Alcohol, Diacetone	1	1	1	3	1	2		1	3		3	3		
Alcohol, Ethl	1	1	1	1	1	1	1	1	3	3	3	1	3	⚠
Alcohol, Isopropyl	1	1	1	1	1	1	1	1	2	1	3	1		
Alcohol, Methyl	1	1	1	1	1	1	1	1	2	1	3	1	1	
Alcohol, Propyl	1	1			1	1	1	1			1	1		
Aluminum Ammonium Sulfate		1	1		1	1	1	1	1	1	1	1	1	
Aluminum Chloride	1	1	1	1	1	1	1	1	1	1	1	1	1	
Aluminum Hydroxide	1	1	1	1	1	1	1	1	1	1	1	2	1	
Aluminum Sulfate (Alum)	1	1	1	1	1	1	1	1	1	1	1	1	1	
Amines	1	1	2	2	2	1	3	1			3	3	3	
Alums	1	1	1	1	1	1	1	2	1	1	1	1	1	
Ammonia, Anhydrous, Liquid	1	1	3	1	1	1	1	1	3	1	3	3	1	
Ammonium Carbonate	1	1	1	2	1	1	1	1	3	1	1	1	1	
Ammonium Chloride 28%	3	1	1	2	1	1	1	2	3	1	1	1	1	
Ammonium Flouride		1	1		1	1	1	1	1	1			1	
Ammonium Hydroxide	1	1	1	1	1	1	1	1	1	1	3	1	3	
Ammonium Nitrate	1	1	1	3	1	1	1	1	1	1	1	1	1	
Ammonium Phosphate	1	1	1	3	1	1	1	3	1	1	1	1	1	
Ammonium Sulfate	1	1	1	3	1	1	1	3	1	1	3	1	1	
Amyl Acetate	1	1	1	3	2	1		1	3	3	3	3	3	⚠
Aniline	1	1	1	1	1	2	2	1	3	2	3	3	3	⚠
Aqua Ammonia		1	1		1	1	1	2	2	1	1	1	1	
Arsenic Acid	1	1	1		2	1	1	3		1	1	1	1	
Barium Carbonate	1	1	1	1	1	1	1	2	1	1	1	1	1	
Barium Chloride	1	1	1	1	1	1	1	2	1	1	1	1	1	
Barium Hydroxide	1	1	1	1	1	1	1	1	1	1	1	1	1	
Barium Sulfate	1	1	1	1		1	1	1	1	1	1	1	1	
Beer	1	1	1	1	1	1	1	1	1	1	1	1	1	
Beet Sugar Liquors		2	1	1	1	1	1	1	1	1	1	1	1	
Benzene	1	1	1	3	3	3	3	1	3	3	1	3	3	⚠
Benzoic Acid	2	1	1	1	1	1	2	2	1	1	1	3	2	
Benzyl Chloride	3	1	1			1	3	2	3	3	1		3	⚠

1 = GOOD   2 = FAIR   3 = UNSATISFACTORY   ☐ = INSUFFICIENT DATA

⚠ **= Do Not Use PE tubing   🚫 = Do Not Use Ceramic Ball**

Chemical or Solution	Hastelloy® C	PTFE/Fluorofilm™	PVDF	Polyprel® (AFLAS™)	Flexiprene™	Polypropylene	PVC	Stainless Steel (316)	Acrylic	Polyethylene	Viton®	Hypalon®	Vinyl	NOTES
Bismuth Carbonate		1	1	1	1	1	1		1	1	1	1	1	
Black Liquor		1	1	1	2	1	1	2	1	1	1	2	1	
Bleach 5.25% Active Chlorine	1	2	1	1	1	2	1	3	1	1	1	1	1	
Borax™	1	1	1	1	1	1	1	2	1	1	1	1	1	
Boric Acid	1	1	1	1	1	1	1	2	1	1	1	1	1	
Bromine Water		1	1	2		2	3	3	3	3	1	1	3	⚠
Bromic Acid		1	1	2	1	1	1			1				
Butylamine	1	1	3	2	2		3	2	3	3	3		3	⚠
Butyl Bromide		1	1		2		3	2	3	3			3	⚠
Butyl Chloride		1	1		2		3	2	3	3			3	⚠
Butyric Acid	1	1	1	1	1			2			2	3		
Calcium Bisulfite	1	1	1	1	1	1		1	1	1	1	1	1	
Calcium Carbonate	1	1	1	1	1	1	1	1	1	1	1	1	1	
Calcium Chlorate		1	1	1	1	1		1	1	1	1	1	1	
Calcium Chloride	1	1	1	1	1	1	1	2	1	1	1	1	1	
Calcium Hydroxide	1	1	1	1	1	1	1	1	1	1	1	1	2	
Calcium Hypochlorite	1	1	1	1	1	2	1	2	1	1	1	1	1	
Calcium Nitrate	1	1	1	1	1	1	1		1	1	1	1	1	
Calcium Sulfate	1	1	1	1	1	1	1	1	1	1	1	1	1	
Carbon Disulfidde		1	1		3	1	3	2	3	3	1	2	3	⚠
Carbon Tetrachloride	1	1	1	3	3	3	2	1	3	3	1	2	2	⚠
Carbonic Acid	1	1	1	1		1	1	1	1	1	1	1	1	
Castor Oil		1	1		1	1	1	1	1	1	1	1	1	
Caustic Soda	1	1	1	1	1	1	1	1	1	1	2	1	2	
Chloral Hydrate		1	1											
Chloroacetic Acid	1	1	1	3	1		3	3		3	3	1	3	⚠
Chlorox™ Bleach 5.25% Active	1	1	1	1	1	2	1	3	1	1	1	1	1	
Chlorobenzene	1	1	1	2	3	2	3	1	3	3	1	3	3	⚠
Chloroform	1	1	1	3	3	3	3	1	3	3	1	3	3	⚠
Chlorosulfonic Acid	1	1	3	2	1	3	2	3		3	3	3	3	⚠
Chrome Alum			1	1	1	1	2	1		1	1	1		
Chromic Acid, 50%	3	1	1	2	1	1		3	3	1	1	1		
Chromic Acid, 30%	3	1	1	2	1	1	1	2	3	1	1	1	1	
Chromic Acid, 10%	1	1	1	2	1	1	1	1	3	1	1	1	1	
Citric Acid	1	1	1	1	1	1	1	1	1	1	1	1	1	
Copper Chloride		1	1	1	1	1	1	3	1	1	1	1	1	
Copper Cyanide	1	1	1	2	1	1	1	1	1	1	1	1	1	
Copper Nitrate	1	1	1	1	1	1	1	1	1	1	1	1	1	
Copper Sulfate	1	1	1	1	1	1	1	1	1	1	1	1	1	
Corn Oil		1	1	1	1	1	1	1	1	1	1	1	1	
Cottonseed Oil		1	1	1	1	1	1	1	1	1	1	1	1	
Cresol	1	1	1	1	2	1	3	1	3	3	2	3	3	⚠
Cresylic Acid	2	1	1	1	2	3	1	1		1	1	3		
Crude Oil		1	1	1	2			2		3	1	3		⚠

1 = GOOD	2 = FAIR	3 = UNSATISFACTORY	☐ = INSUFFICIENT DATA

⚠ = Do Not Use PE tubing   🚫 = Do Not Use Ceramic Ball

Chemical or Solution	Hastelloy C	PTFE/Fluorofilm	PVDF	Polyprel (AFLAS)	Flexiprene	Polypropylene	PVC	Stainless Steel (316)	Acrylic	Polyethylene	Viton	Hypalon	Vinyl	NOTES
Dextrose	1	1	1	1	1	1	1	1	1	1	1	1	1	
Detergents, General	1	1	1	2	1	1	1	1	1	1	1	1	1	
Dibutyl Phthalate	1	1	1	2	2	2	3		3	3	3	3	3	⚠
Dichloroethene	1	2		3	2			1			2	3		⚠
Diesel Fuel	1	1	1	1	2		1	1	1	2	1	1	1	⚠
Diethylene Glycol	2	2		1	1	1		1			1	1		⚠
Dimethyl Formamide	1	1	3	3	2	1	3	1	3	1	3		3	
Dinitrotoluene		1		3	1			1			3	3		⚠
Dioctyl Phthalate		2	2	1	2	2			3	3	2	3		⚠
Disodium Phosphate		1	1			1	1				1	1		⚠
Ethanol, 1-95%	1	1	1	1	1	1	1	2	1	1	3	1	1	
Ethers	2	1		3	2	2	3	1	3		3	3	3	⚠
Ethyl Acetate	1	1	3	3	2	2	3	1	3	3	3	3	3	⚠
Ethyl Chloride		1	1	1	2	2	3	1	3	3	3	3	3	⚠
Ethyl Ether	2	1		3	1	2	3	1	3	3	3	3	3	⚠
Ethylene Chloride		1	1	1		2	3	1	3	3	2	3	3	⚠
Ethylenediamine	3	1	2	2	1		3	2	3	3	3		3	⚠
Ethylene Dichloride	1	1	1	1	2	2		1			1	3		⚠
Ethylene Glycol	2	1	1	1	1	1	1	1	1	1	1	1	1	
Ethylene Oxide	1	1	3	3	1	2		1			3	3		⚠
Fatty Acid	1	1	1	2	1	1	1	1	1	1	1	3	1	
Ferric Chloride	1	1	1	1	1	1	1	3	1	1	1	1	1	
Ferric Nitrate	2	1	1	1	1	1	1	1	1	1	1	1	1	
Ferric Sulfate	1	1	1	1	1	1	1	2	1	1	1	1	1	
Ferrous Chloride	2	1	1	1	1	1	1	3	1	1	1	1	1	
Ferrous Sulfate	1	1	1	1	1	1	1	3	1	1	1	1	1	
Fluoboric Acid	1	1	1		1	1		2		1	1			⚠
Fluosilicic Acid	1	1	1	1	1	1	1	2	1	1	1	1	1	⊘
Formaldehyde	1	1	1	3	1	1	1	2	1	1	3	2	1	
Formic Acid	1	1	1	1	1	1	2	2	1	1	2	1	3	
Fruit Juice Pulp	1	1	1	1	1	1	1	1	1	1	1	1	1	
Fuel Oil	1	1	1	1	1	2		1	1	2	1	3		⚠
Gallic Acid	2	1	1	2	1	1	1	1		1	1	2		
Gasoline, Refined	1	1	1	2	2	2	1	2	1	1	1	1	1	
Glucose	1	1	1	1	1	1	1	1	1	1	1	1	1	
Glycerine or Glycerol	1	1	1	1	1	1	1	1	1	1	1	1	1	
Glycolic Acid, 30%	1	1	1	2	1	1		1		1	1	1		
Heptane	1	1	1	3	3	2		1			1	1	2	⚠
Hexane	1	1	1	3	2	2		1			1	2	2	⚠
Hexanol, Tertiary	1	1	1		2	1	3	1		1	1	2	2	
Hydrazine		1	1	2	1			1			1	1		⚠
Hydrobromic Acid, 20%	1	1	1	1	1	1	1	3	1	1	1	1	1	
Hydrochloric Acid, Concentrate	3	1	1	1	1	1	1	3	1	1	1	3	2	
Hydrochloric Acid, Dilute	2	1	1	1	1	1	1	3	1	1	1	2	1	

1 = GOOD   2 = FAIR   3 = UNSATISFACTORY   ☐ = INSUFFICIENT DATA
⚠ = Do Not Use PE tubing   ⊘ = Do Not Use Ceramic Ball

Chemical or Solution	Hastelloy® C	PTFE/Fluorofilm™	PVDF	Polyprel® (AFLAS™)	Flexiprene™	Polypropylene	PVC	Stainless Steel (316)	Acrylic	Polyethylene	Viton®	Hypalon®	Vinyl	NOTES
Hydrocyanic Acid	1	1		1	1	1	1	2		1	1	1		
Hydrofluoric Acid	1	1	1	1	1	1	2	3	3	1	1	1		⊘
Hydrofluosillicic Acid	1	1	1	1	1	1	2	1	1	1	1	1	1	⊘
Hydrogen Peroxide, 90%	1	1	1	3	3	2	1	2	3	2	1	2		⚠
Hydrogen Peroxide, 50%	1	1	1	2	2	2	1	1	3	2	1	1		⚠
Hydrogen Sulfide, Aqueous	1	1	1	1	1	1	1	2	1	1	3	1	1	
Hypochlorous Acid	1	1	1	1	1	1	1			1	1	3	1	
Iodine Water Solution		1	1	1	1	1	2	3	1	2	1	1	2	⚠
Kerosene	1	1	1	2	2	2	1	1	1	2	1	3		⚠
Lactic Acid	2	1	1	1	1	1	1	2	1	1	1	1	1	
Lard Oil	1	1	1	1	1	1	1	1	1	1	1	3	1	
Lauric Acid		1	1	2	1	2	1							⚠
Lead Acetate	2	1	1	3	1	1	1	2		1	3	3		
Linoleic Acid		1	1	2	1	2	1	1			2	3		⚠
Linseed Oil	1	1	1	1	1	2	1			3	1	2	1	⚠
Lithium Salts		1	1	1	1		1			1				
Magnesium Carbonate	1	1	1	1	1	1	1	1	1	1	1	2	1	
Magnesium Chloride	1	1	1	1	1	1	1	3	1	1	1	1	1	
Magnesium Hydroxide	1	1	1	1	1	1	1	1	1	1	1	1	1	
Magnesium Nitrate	1	1	1	1	1	1	1	1	1	1	1	1	1	
Magnesium Oxide		1	1	1	1	1	1	1	1	1	2	1	1	
Magnesium Sulfate	1	1	1	1	1	1	1	1	1	1	1	1	1	
Maleic Acid	1	1	1	1	1	1	1	1		1	1	3		
Malic Acid	1	1	1	2	1	1	1	1		1	1	1		
Mercuric Chloride	3	1	1	1	1	1	1	3		1	1	1		
Methanol	1	1	1	1	1	1	1	1	3	1	3	1	1	
Methyl Ethyl Ketone	1	1	3	3	2	2	3	1	3		3	3		⚠
Methyl Isobutyl Ketone	1	1	3	3	2	2	3	1	3	3	3	3	3	⚠
Methyl Isopropyl Ketone		1	3	3	2		3	1	3		3	3	3	⚠
Methyl Sulfate		1	1			3	1		3	1			3	
Milk	1	1	1	1	1	1	1	1	1	1	1	1	1	
Mineral Oil	1	1	1	1	2	2	1	1	1	1	1	1	1	
Naptha, Petroleum	1	1	1	1	3	2	1	2	1	3	1	3	1	⚠
Napthalene	1	1	1	3	3	2	3	1		3	1	3	3	⚠
Nickel Chloride	1	1	1	1	1	1	1	2	1	1	1	1	1	
Nickel Sulfate	1	1	1	1	1	1	1	2	1	1	1	1	1	
Nitric Acid, Anhydrous		1	1	2	2	3	1	2	3	3	2	3	3	⚠
Nitric Acid, 68%	2	1	1	2	2	2	1	2	3	3	1	3	2	⚠
Nitric Acid, 10%	1	1	1	1	1	1	1	1	3	1	1	2	2	
Oils and Fats	1	1	1			1	1	1	1	1				
Oleic Acid	1	1	1	1	1	1	1	1		1	1	2	2	
Oleum	3	1	3	3	3	3	3	2	3	3	1	3	3	⚠
Olive Oil	1	1	1	1	1	1	1	2	1	1	1	1	1	
Oxalic Acid	1	1	1	1	1	1	1	2	1	1	1	1	1	

1 = GOOD   2 = FAIR   3 = UNSATISFACTORY   ☐ = INSUFFICIENT DATA
⚠ = Do Not Use PE tubing   ⊘ = Do Not Use Ceramic Ball

Chemical or Solution	Hastelloy® C	PTFE/Fluorofilm™	PVDF	Polyprel® (AFLAS™)	Flexiprene™	Polypropylene	PVC	Stainless Steel (316)	Acrylic	Polyethylene	Viton®	Hypalon®	Vinyl	NOTES
Palmitric Acid	1	1	1	1	1	1	1	1		1	1	2		
Perchloric Acid, 70%	1	1	1	2		1	1	3	3	1	1	2	2	
Perchloric Acid, 10%	1	1	1	2	1	1	1	3	3	1	1	2	1	
Perchloroethylene	1	1	1	3	3		1	1	3	3	1	3	3	⚠
Petroleum Oils (Sour)		1	1	2	3	2	1	2	1	3	1	2	1	⚠
Phenol	1	1	1	1	1	1	1	2	3	3	1	3	3	⚠
Phosphoric Acid, 50%	1	1	1	1	1	1	1	3	1	1	1	2	1	
Phosphoric Acid, 25%	1	1	1	1	1	1	1	3	1	1	1	1	1	
Photographic Solution	2	1	1	2	1	1	1	1	1	1	1	1	1	
Phthalic Acid	2	1	1	2	1	1	1	1	1	1			1	
Picric Acid	1	1	1	1	1	2	3	1	1	2	1	1	1	⚠
Plating Solution	1	1	1	1	1	1	1	1		1	1	3	1	
Potassium Carbonate	1	1	1	1	1	1	1	2	1	1	1	1	1	
Potassium Bromide	1	1	1	1	1	1	1	1	1	1	1	1	1	
Potassium Chlorate	1	1	1	1	1	1	1	1	1	1	1	1	1	
Potassium Chloride	1	1	1	1	1	1	1	2	1	1	1	1	1	
Potassium Dichromate	1	1	1	1	1	1	1	2	1	1	1	1	1	
Potassium Ferrocyanide	1	1	1	1	1	1	1	2	1	1	1	1	1	
Potassium Hydroxide (KOH)	2	1	1	1	1	1	1	1	1	1	3	1	2	
Potassium Nitrate	2	1	1	1	1	1	1	1	1	1	1	1	1	
Potassium Permanganate, 10%	1	1	1	1	1	1	1	1	1	1	1	1	1	
Potassium Phosphate	1	1	1	1	1	1	1	1	1	1	1	1	1	
Potassium Sulfate	2	1	1	1	1	1	1	1	1	1	1	1	1	
Propylene Dichloride	2	1	1		2	2	3		2	3			3	⚠
Pyridine	1	1	1	3	2	1		1	3		3	3		⚠
Sea Water	1	1	1	1	1	1	1	3	1	1	1	1	1	
Silver Nitrate	1	1	1	1	1	1	1	1	1	1	1	1	1	
Silver Plating Solutions	1	1	1	1	1	1	1	1	1	1	1		1	
Soaps	1	1	1	1	1	1	1	2	1	1	1	1	1	
Sodium Acetate	1	1	1	3	1	1	1	1	1	1	3	3		
Sodium Bicarbonate	2	1	1	1	1	1	1	1	1	1	1	1	1	
Sodium Bisulfate	2	1	1	1	1	1	1	3	1	1	1	1	1	
Sodium Bisulfite	1	1	1	1	1	1	1	2	1	1	1	1	1	
Sodium Carbonate	1	1	1	1	1	1	1	2	1	1	1	1	1	
Sodium Borate	1	1	1	1	1	1	1		1	1	1	1	1	
Sodium Chlorate	2	1	1		1	1	1	2	1	1	1	1	2	
Sodium Chloride	1	1	1	1	1	1	1	2	1	1		1	1	
Sodium Cyanide	1	1	1	1	1	1	1	2	1	1	1			
Sodium Fluoride	1	1	1	1	1	1	1	3	1	1	1	1	1	🚫
Sodium Ferrocyanide	1	1	2	1	1	1	1	2		1	1	1		
Sodium Hexametaphosphate		2	1	1	1	1	1	1	1	1	1	1	1	
Sodium Hydroxide, Caustic	1	2	1	1	1	1	1	2	1	2	1	2		
Sodium Hypochlorite, 12.5%	1	1	1	1	1	3	1	3	1	1	1	1	1	
Sodium Metaphosphate		1	1	1	1	1	1	1	1	1	1	1	1	

1 = GOOD   **2 = FAIR**   **3 = UNSATISFACTORY**   ☐ **= INSUFFICIENT DATA**

⚠ **= Do Not Use PE tubing**   🚫 **= Do Not Use Ceramic Ball**

Chemical or Solution	Hastelloy® C	PTFE/Fluorofilm™	PVDF	Polyprel® (AFLAS™)	Flexiprene™	Polypropylene	PVC	Stainless Steel (316)	Acrylic	Polyethylene	Viton®	Hypalon®	Vinyl	NOTES
Sodium Nitrate	1	1	1	3	1	1	1	1	1	1	1	1	1	
Sodium Peroxide	1	1	1	2	1		1			1	1	1	1	
Sodium Phosphate	1	1	1	1	1	1	1	2	1	1	1	1	1	
Sodium Silicate	1	1	1	1	1	1	1	1	1	1	1	1	1	
Sodium Sulfate	1	1	1	1	1	1	1	1	1	1	1	1	1	
Sodium Sulfide	2	1	1	1	1	1	1	3		1	1	1	1	
Sodium Sulfite	1	1	1	1	1	1	1	2		1	1	1	1	
Sodium Thiosulfate	1	1	1	1	1	1	1			1	1	1	1	
Sour Crude Oil		1	1	2	3	2	1			3			1	⚠
Stannic Chloride	1	1	1			1	1	3		1	1	3		
Stannous Chloride	1	1	1		1	1	1	2		1	1	1		
Stearic Acid	1	1	1	1	1	1	1	1		1	1	1	1	
Sulfur	1	1	1	1	1	1	1	1	1	1	1	2	1	
Sulfer Trioxide		1	3	1		2	1	3		3	1	3		⚠
Sulfuric Acid, 10%	2	1	1	1	1	1	1	3	1	1	1	2	1	
Sulfuric Acid, 75%	2	1	1	1	1	2	1	3	3	2	1	2	2	⚠
Sulfuric Acid, 98.5%	3	1	1	1	1	2	1	3	3	2	1	2	3	⚠
Sulfurous Acid	1	1	1	1	1	1	1	3		1	1	1		
Tannic Acid	2	1	1	2	1	1	1	1		1	1	1		
Tanning Liquors	1	1	1	1	1	1	1			1	1			
Tartaric Acid	1	1	1	2	1	1	1			1	1	1		
Tetrachlorethane	1	1	1	3	3			1			1	3		⚠
Tetrahydrofuran	1	1	3	3	1	2	3			3	3	3		⚠
Tetraethyl Lead		1	1	3	1	1	1				1	3		⚠
Tetralin		1	1		3	2	1		3	2	1		1	⚠
Tin Salts	3	1	1	1	1	1	1		1	1		1	1	
Toluene	1	1	1	3	3	3	3	1	3	3	1	3	3	⚠
Trichloroethylene	1	1	1	3	3	3	3	2	3	3	1	3	3	⚠
Triethanolamine	1	1	1	3	1	1	2			2	3	2		⚠
Turpentine	1	1	1	1	3	2	3	1	3	3	1	3	3	⚠
Vinegar	1	1	1	1	1	1	1	1	1	1	1	1	1	
Vegetable Oils	1	1	1	1	1	1	1	1	1	1	1	3	1	
Water, Acid, Mine	1	1	1	1	1	1	1	1	1	1	1	1	1	
Water, Fresh	1	1	1	1	1	1	1	1	1	1	1	1	1	
Water, Distilled	1	1	1	1	1	1	1	1	1	1	1	1	1	
Water, Salt	1	1	1	1	1	1	2	1	1	1	1	1	1	
Whiskey		1	1	1	1	1	1	1	1	1	1	1	1	
Wines		1	1	1	1	1	1	1	1	1	1	1	1	
Xylene	1	1	1	3	3	2	3		3	3	1	1	3	⚠
Zinc Chloride	1	1	1	1	1	1	1	3	1	1	1	1	1	
Zinc Sulfate	1	1	1	1	1	1	1	2	1	1	1	1	1	

1 = GOOD   2 = FAIR   3 = UNSATISFACTORY   ☐ = INSUFFICIENT DATA
⚠ = Do Not Use PE tubing   ⊘ = Do Not Use Ceramic Ball

DISCLAIMER OF WARRANTY AND LIABILITY

Although the information set forth herein is presented in good faith and believed to be correct on the date of issuance, Liquid Metronics Incorporated makes no guarantee or representation as to the completeness or accuracy thereof, and disclaims all liability for any loss or damage resulting from use or reliance upon any information, recommendations or suggestions contained herein. **LIQUID METRONICS INCORPORATED MAKES NO EXPRESS OR IMPLIED REPRESENTATIONS OR WARRANTIES AS TO THE FITNESS, MERCHANTABILITY, OR ANY OTHER MATTER WITH RESPECT TO THE INFORMATION CONTAINED HEREIN OR ANY PRODUCT OR SUBSTANCE REFERRED TO HEREIN,** whether used alone or in combination with any other material. Nothing contained herein is to be construed as a recommendation to use any product in conflict with any patent.

The data in all tables are based on samples tested and are not guaranteed for all samples or other applications. Write to us for our current sales specifications.

LMI
MILTON ROY

8 Post Office Square
Acton, MA 01720 USA
TEL: (978) 263-9800
FAX: (978) 264-9172
http://www.lmipumps.com

Replaces same of Rev. E 10/97
1100.F 4/01

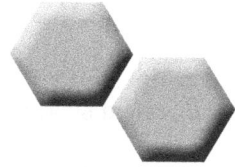

Index

Note: *f.* indicates figure.

www.ingramcontent.com/pod-product-compliance
Lightning Source LLC
Chambersburg PA
CBHW070736220326
41598CB00024BA/3441